1 The Allocation of Resources

2 Making Best Use of Resources

3 Purchasing Better Mental Health Services

Contents

© Crown Copyright 1994
Application for reproduction should be made to HMSO

Printed in the UK for the Audit Commission at Beacon Press, Uckfield
ISBN 011 886 143 3

London: HMSO

Cover photograph by Hilary Shedel
With thanks to Dorothy

Preface

The Audit Commission oversees the external audit of local authorities and agencies within the National Health Service (NHS) in England and Wales. As part of this function the Commission is charged with reviewing the economy, efficiency and effectiveness of services provided by these bodies. To this end, studies and audits of selected topics are undertaken each year.

The study of mental health services follows from previous reviews of community care, which focused on health and social care for all client groups and led to reports such as *Making a Reality of Community Care*, *The Cascade of Change*, *The Community Revolution* and *Homeward Bound*. The Commission has now begun a series of studies of the care for specific groups, of which this is one. The study has been limited to services for adults with mental health problems and does not cover specialties such as drug and alcohol abuse services. Care for children and elderly people with mental health problems will be the subjects of future studies.

The study on which this report is based was carried out by a team, directed by David Browning, consisting of Judy Renshaw and Caroline Gardner, with considerable assistance from Vida Field. Kirti Patel and Penny Hammond undertook much of the data preparation and analysis. Geraldine Strathdee was the external consultant to the study. Helen Wood and Good Practices in Mental Health carried out the survey of users' views with advice and guidance from Marion Beeforth and Edna Conlan.

Introduction

1. Mental health problems are a major cause of disruption and difficulty in people's lives. In any one year more than a quarter of all people suffer to some degree. Most visit their GP, usually for other reasons, although less than half are recognised as having a mental health problem. Most recover over a period of weeks or months and are best helped by 'ordinary' services in a setting which everyone uses, such as the GP surgery. Only those with the most serious conditions need specialised care or admission to hospital (Exhibit 1).

2. Mental illness is not a single condition but a range of disorders from severely disabling conditions to more minor emotional distress. The distinction between more and less severe mental health problems is not necessarily based on diagnosis (Ref. 2) although psychotic illnesses like schizophrenia are the most likely to lead to serious and long-term disability. Three broad need groups can be identified: those with long-term needs for care, most of whom will have either spent long periods in hospital or experienced many short admissions in a so-called 'revolving door' pattern; those with severe mental disorders who may have experienced hospital admission at some time; and those with acute episodes of distress, such as anxiety and depression. Suicide is more common among people known to have mental health problems than the rest of the population and most people who commit suicide have been suffering from some form of mental illness.

Exhibit 1
The prevalence of mental health problems

Only those with the most serious problems need specialised care or admission to hospital.

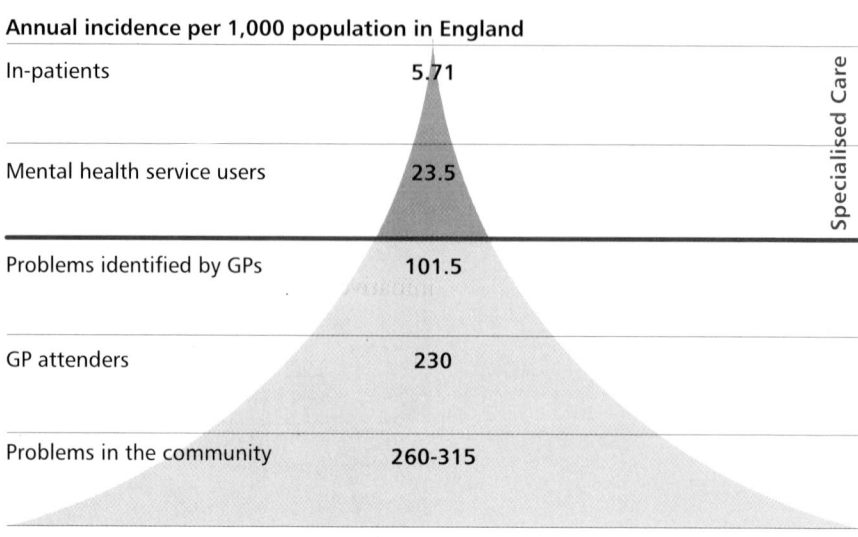

Annual incidence per 1,000 population in England

In-patients	5.71	Specialised Care
Mental health service users	23.5	
Problems identified by GPs	101.5	
GP attenders	230	
Problems in the community	260-315	

Source:
Goldberg and Huxley (Ref. 1).

Mental health care policy

'The Department of Health's policy goal is now that specialist psychiatric services should target their efforts on severely mentally ill people'

3. Mental health services have multiple aims: treatment to help people recover; care for those with continuing problems to help to limit their disabilities and maximise their potential for an ordinary life; and protection of the public from anyone who is likely to pose a risk. Measurement of outcomes is difficult because many different dimensions (symptoms, activities, morale and quality of life) have to be taken into account. Mental health services cannot prevent people from developing severe mental illness but social factors such as housing, employment and education may have an impact.

4. The policy for dealing with mental health problems has changed. For many years, care was provided in large remote hospitals but from about the time of the 1959 Mental Health Act the aim has been to provide care for most people in the community, supported by hospitals when necessary. Community care is preferred since it is more accessible and causes less disruption to peoples' lives. The 1975 white paper, *Better Services for the Mentally Ill* (Ref. 3), described a model district service that replaced care in large psychiatric hospitals with local hospital beds and a range of accommodation and services in the community. Resettlement of the long-stay residents of institutions has been encouraged. A care programme approach (CPA) for the assessment, coordination and review of care for individuals and a specific grant to local authorities for social care for people with serious mental illness (MISG, £31 million in 1992/93) were introduced in 1991 to provide further support for people in the community (Refs. 4, 5). In 1992 mental illness was chosen as a key area for the government paper, *Health of the Nation* (Ref. 6), with targets set for improving the health and social functioning of mentally ill people and reducing the suicide rate.

5. The Department of Health's policy goal is now that specialist psychiatric services should target their efforts on severely mentally ill people to ensure that they receive the treatment, care and follow-up that they need and do not drift out of contact with services. The CPA has been supplemented by supervision registers, designed for those most at risk of harming themselves or others, or of self-neglect, and who need particular care and follow-up. Purchasers have also been told to address the issue of targeting in contracts. A number of initiatives to assist primary care services in helping those who are less severely ill are underway, including support for a senior GP fellow in continuing medical education of GPs and for the 'defeat depression' campaign of the Royal Colleges.

6. The policy in Wales is slightly different in form, although many of the principles are similar. The strategy for mental illness services (Ref. 7), which places community teams as the focus of the service, has been updated by the 1993 *Protocol for Investment in Health Gain* (Ref. 8). This has outlined a number of additional goals including:

- reduction of the impact of socio-economic factors on mental distress and relapse associated with mental illness; and
- reduction of the stigma attached to mental health problems.

Exhibit 2
The number of hospital beds

The number of beds has declined markedly since the 1950s.

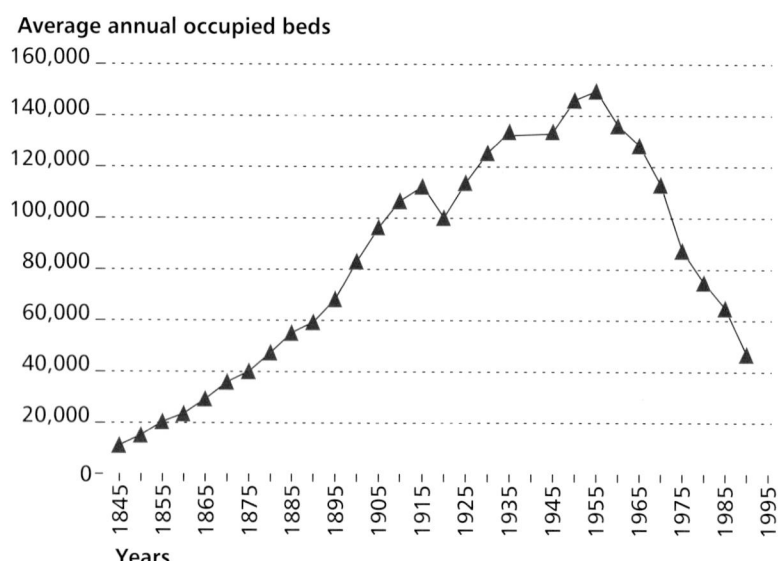

Average annual occupied beds

Source:
Inter-authority Comparisons and Consultancy: data for England and Wales.

A changing service

Exhibit 3
Length of stay in hospital

Shorter stays have become more common.

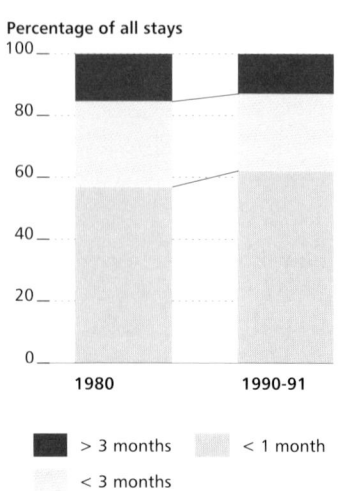

Percentage of all stays

> 3 months   < 1 month

< 3 months

Source:
Department of Health, Health and Personal Social Services statistics 1993.

7. The balance of care has begun to shift away from the large psychiatric hospitals. The number of beds has declined markedly since the 1950s (Exhibit 2), especially in the larger hospitals.

8. The resettlement of most of the 'old long-stay' residents of hospitals has presented few problems where this has been part of a planned programme of reprovision and money has been transferred with individuals, although people with challenging behaviour or physical problems have tended to get left behind. Of the old institutions (130 in 1960) 92 are still open, with lower and lower occupancy rates and steadily increasing unit costs. The Government has appointed a task force to assist with the closure programme and to facilitate the development of better services in the community. Consequently, the Commission has not reviewed the closure process in detail. A new pattern of services for acute care is beginning to develop and shorter lengths of stay have become more common (Exhibit 3). The number of community-based teams has multiplied throughout the 1980s. The key professionals involved in these teams are described briefly in the glossary at the end of this report. In spite of this progress, good comprehensive community care for people with mental health problems is slow to develop and its lack of implementation is causing major concern.

9. Part of the reason for this slow progress is that most of the money remains in the hospital sector. In 1992/93 £1.8 billion was spent on adult mental health services in England and Wales. Most of this was in the NHS, with two thirds of the total spent on in-patient care (Exhibit 4). £185 million was spent in local authorities, including a specific grant of £31 million. In addition, nearly £20 million was spent on private and voluntary residential care, supported by social security payments. The NHS contribution amounts to almost ten per cent of the total hospital and community health service budget for England.

6

Is the policy failing?

10. A popular perception is that community care is not working and that it is the cause both of danger to the public and of more mentally ill people on the streets. Mentally disturbed individuals have, on two occasions recently, climbed into the lions' den at London Zoo. Ben Silcock, a former psychiatric patient suffering from schizophrenia, did this after discharging himself from treatment. In the most recent case Tony Sarumi, the man concerned, had refused treatment after one day in hospital and was not considered to be sufficiently at risk to be compulsorily detained. No alternative treatment or support appears to have been offered at that time. Mentally ill people can occasionally be dangerous to others too. In 1992 Jonathan Zito, a complete stranger, was fatally stabbed by Christopher Clunis, a man who had also been diagnosed as having schizophrenia. The Ritchie Report on this tragic incident (Ref. 9) was highly critical of most of the services and individuals involved in his care. The Boyd inquiry (Ref. 10) has identified 34 people in an 18-month period who had been receiving psychiatric treatment during the year before committing a homicide, although it pointed out that these numbers are very small in comparison with either the total number of homicides or the number receiving psychiatric help. Such incidents have thrown a spotlight on the shift to providing more care in local community settings and relying less on the old mental hospitals, even though much of the criticism is based on a misinterpretation of current policy. Some have even questioned the appropriateness of the change; the Secretary of State for Health has said, in response to the Christopher Clunis Inquiry, that 'the pendulum has swung too far'.

11. Others argue, however, that it has not yet gone far enough. They point out that two thirds of expenditure is still locked up in hospitals and only one third is available for community care. They say that with proper community services and procedures to minimise risks such tragedies could be avoided.

12. So who is right? It is a contentious area but two facts stand out. First, although the few who are dangerous need special attention in order to avoid any further tragedies, most people with schizophrenia lead relatively normal lives. Many are quiet and withdrawn and find it hard to cope with the demands of everyday life. They are likely to have difficulty with their housing, finances and social relationships. In the last two decades of the community care policy the number of homicides committed by mentally ill people has not increased while the number committed by others has more than doubled (Ref. 11).

13. The second fact is that people receiving community care, however inadequate, hardly ever wish to return to hospital. Psychiatric hospital care seems to be strongly disliked by most of those who have experienced it (although many admit that a short spell in hospital may have been necessary). Common complaints from users are the lack of privacy, the inadequacy of care plans and the lack of contact with professional staff. This is not to say that community services are able to provide the answer yet. GPs and primary care teams need better support. Users often ask for better access to specialist services outside of office hours and crisis alternatives which do not involve

Exhibit 4
Expenditure on mental health services

Most NHS expenditure is on in-patient care.

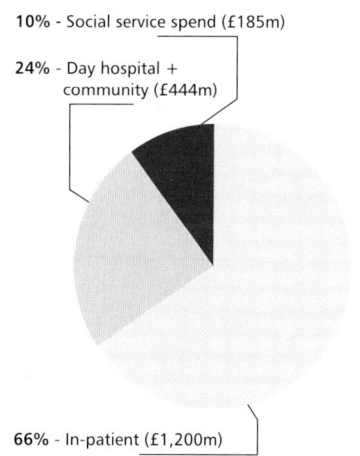

10% - Social service spend (£185m)

24% - Day hospital + community (£444m)

66% - In-patient (£1,200m)

Sources: Department of Health statistics, Welsh Office Health and Personal Social Services statistics, CIPFA - data for England and Wales, 1992/93

'Psychiatric hospital care seems to be strongly disliked by most of those who have experienced it...'

hospital. They want more practical help with employment, housing and benefits than they currently receive. The needs of minority ethnic groups are not well addressed by mental health services; many of these people enter services via the police or crisis services and tend to move into secure and locked facilities more often than their white counterparts. The carers and relatives of people with mental health problems frequently complain about the lack of information about services and treatments and about professionals not paying sufficient attention to their needs.

14. The Audit Commission has undertaken a review of services for people with mental health needs, excluding children, older people with dementia and those with drug or alcohol problems. Twelve districts in England and Wales were visited by the research team and a survey carried out by auditors in ninety NHS provider agencies. This report sets out the findings. The main focus has been on NHS providers and social services departments; information has also been gathered about independent providers, although they do not come within the scope of the local audits.

15. The Commission has concluded that the way forward is to strengthen the leadership and management of the service. Shifting from a hospital-based to a largely community-based service is difficult but the process is now fairly well researched and understood. However, apart from a few exceptional individuals, there has been nobody in a position to drive the changes through, despite widespread agreement with the policy. If locally-based mental health care is to work effectively, the whole process of closing the old long-stay hospitals and of setting up new community-based services needs strong, vigorous and coherent leadership. The Government needs to reaffirm its commitment to comprehensive local services and to coordinate the responsibilities of the Departments of Health, Environment, Education, Employment, Social Security and the Home Office in this area, as pointed out by the Mental Health Foundation in their recent report (Ref. 12). Health purchasers, after negotiation with providers, need to specify more clearly what is required, with explicit targets and timescales for their achievement. Providers need clear leadership by competent managers with appropriate skills, who can work with professionals and others to enable constructive change to take place.

16. The main challenges are identified in this report. In Chapter 1 the pattern of resource distribution is reviewed. In Chapter 2 the targeting and management of those services are examined. In Chapter 3 the implications for commissioning authorities are set out and the coordination of the different agencies is examined. Local audits of mental health services will take place during 1995 to help identify an agenda for change in each authority.

The Audit Commission has reviewed progress and concluded that the way forward is to strengthen leadership and management. The issues confronting authorities are set out in the following chapters.

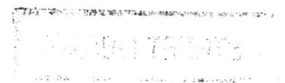

1 The Allocation of Resources

Local needs vary.
Some districts need four times as many mental health resources as others but the allocation of resources to districts does not match the pattern of local needs.

The balance of resources within districts is not appropriate.
Most of the resources for mental health are tied up in hospital care. Community services are patchy.

Users and carers want more and better community services.
Few districts have a good mix of suitable services such as crisis care, out-of-hours services, respite care and employment.

£40m could be saved or 6,000 extra staffed housing places provided by rationalising the balance of supported accommodation.

£13m could be released (or two million extra hours of care provided in the community) by rationalising the skill mix of community-based staff.

17. Mental health services in some inner city areas are undoubtedly under pressure. Reflecting this, hospitals in the most socially-deprived boroughs in Britain (as indicated by census data) have enormous demand on their psychiatric beds. Hospitals in most suburban and rural areas are not under anything like the same pressure. One indicator of this is the difference in the number of people who are 'sectioned' (admitted to hospital against their will). An inner city hospital has much greater pressure on its beds from compulsory admissions (Exhibit 5). These dramatic differences between different parts of the country explain why there are such divergent popular views. Resources vary but not always in line with need.

The needs of different populations

18. The need for mental health care varies widely with local characteristics, particularly with social deprivation, leading to a four or fivefold difference in the need for resources in different areas (Ref. 13). Such resources include social care and housing as well as NHS care. Hospital admission rates for different populations – a good 'proxy' for need – vary by a factor of five and are associated with social factors such as the number of people living alone and in poverty. A reasonably accurate way of predicting admission rates is based on Brian Jarman's underprivileged area scores – the so-called Jarman 8, which combines eight of these social factors (Refs. 14, 15). Other indicators of need, such as the bed occupancy levels of acute psychiatric wards (Ref. 16), the number of violent incidents (Ref. 17) and the number of 'new long-stay' patients who have remained in hospital for over a year (Ref. 18), are also associated with the Jarman 8 scores for London districts. Unemployment rates are associated with hospital admission in small areas such as electoral wards (Ref.19).

19. A recent report (Ref. 13) has examined the relationship between need and resources in part of London and an adjoining county. The number of people who were single, widowed or divorced, living in a household without a car, or who were unemployed or permanently sick were the best predictors of the number of admissions to hospital. The most significant factors differed between London and the county. One of the main conclusions was that the admissions were lower in London than would have been predicted by the model, implying that people admitted in the county would not be in London. This may reflect differences in pressure on beds in the two areas and is supported by the report of the task force on services in London (Ref. 20).

20. A population study in London has also found the prevalence of schizophrenia to be associated with social deprivation (Refs. 21, 22). In this case mental health problems were measured directly, without confounding them with service responses.

21. The needs of many different kinds of people have to be taken into account when allocating resources. Some require a specially intensive resource because of the severity of their problems while others, such as ethnic minority groups, have needs that require different types of response.

Exhibit 5
Compulsory admissions to two hospitals

The inner city hospital has much greater pressure on its beds from compulsory admissions.

Inner City Hospital

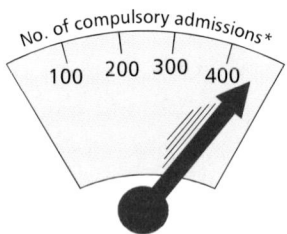

Rural Hospital

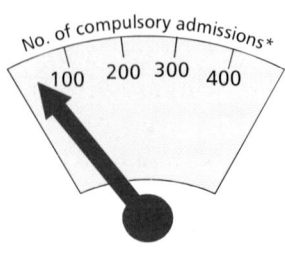

*per 100,000 population
(1993/94)

Source: Compulsory admissions data for two hospitals.

Examples of specific needs include:

- A small number of people who pose a risk to others or who have challenging behaviour require care in a secure setting. People detained under the Mental Health Act, for whom a code of practice is in operation, need special consideration.

- Mentally disordered offenders should now be cared for by health and social services on the basis that their condition demands care and treatment rather than a punitive response. The diversion of large numbers of these people into the mental health services has significant resource implications.

- Many homeless people have mental health problems. Most have experienced brief admissions to hospital, only to lose touch with services later, and very few are former long-stay residents. The number of homeless people in an area can dramatically affect the pressures on hospitals; admission rates can be twenty times the rate for people in stable housing (Ref. 23).

- People from ethnic minority groups require special consideration by mental health services if their needs are to be addressed adequately. Black African-Caribbean people are admitted more frequently than the proportion of their number in the population would imply (Ref. 24, 25). Irish people also have a higher than expected admission rate. Asian people, on the other hand, appear to experience delayed entry into the mental health services until a crisis point is reached, possibly because they are more reluctant than others to reveal their symptoms to GPs. Black peoples' experiences of mental health services are often more traumatic and less helpful than those of white people, partly because of a lack of cross-cultural understanding by professionals (Ref. 26). They may possibly have a higher incidence of certain illnesses (Ref. 27). Womens' experiences of mental health services can be particularly harrowing. Living on a mixed ward is unacceptable for many, especially certain religious groups.

- Facilities for mothers with young babies are sometimes necessary in order to avoid separating them at a vulnerable time.

Exhibit 6
Resources and needs

Expenditure is not closely related to need.

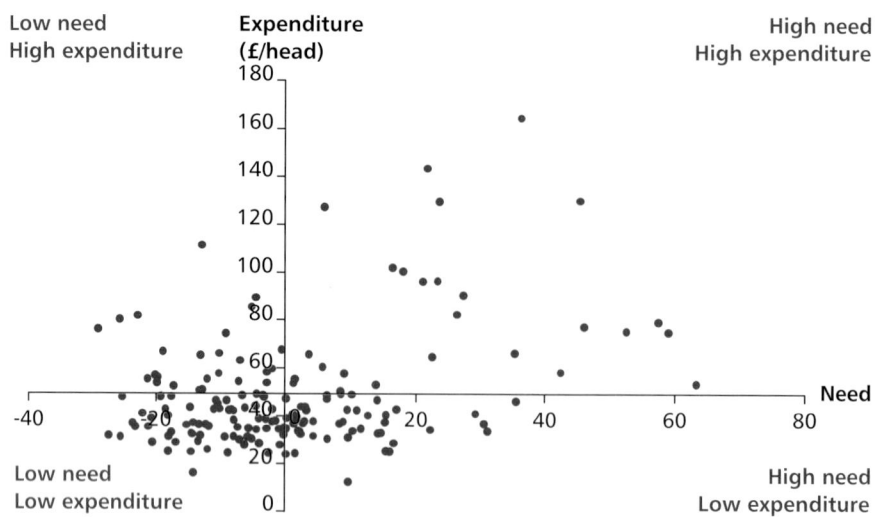

*Sources: Department of Health, Health and
Personal Social Services statistics 1992/93, Jarman*

Matching resources to needs

Matching resources to needs between districts

22. Expenditure is not closely related to need (Exhibit 6). Districts have widely differing needs for mental health care; some of the most deprived inner city districts appear to need four times the resources that others do. The Jarman index gives an indication of the likely need. Many districts with a higher than average expenditure are comparatively well-to-do on the basis of the Jarman score (the top left hand section of Exhibit 6). On the contrary, many which spend comparatively little on mental health care are highly deprived (the bottom right hand section of Exhibit 6). The mental health task force has also argued for more resources for severely ill people in parts of London.

Exhibit 7
Historical patterns of spending

Districts which used to run large hospitals still spend more on mental health care for their population.

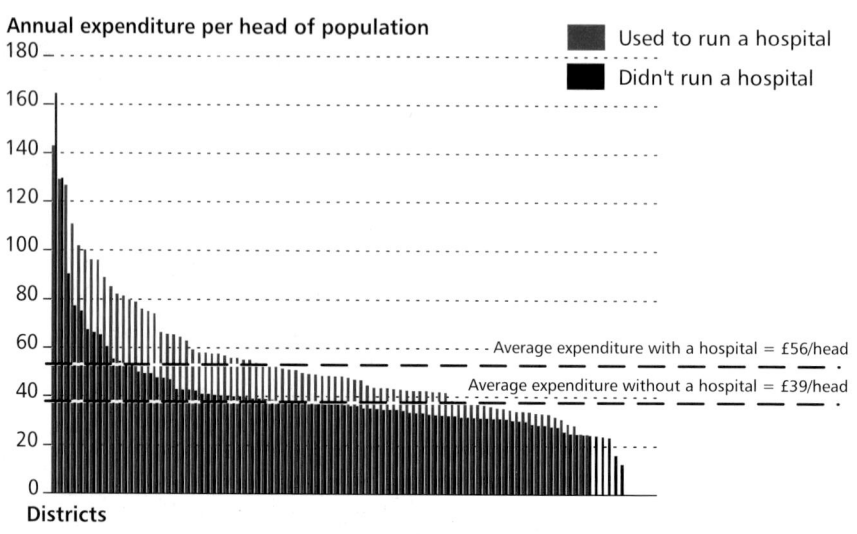

*Sources: Inter-Authority Comparisons and
Consultancy, Department of Health, Health and
Personal Social Services statistics 1992/93.*

23. One underlying cause of this mismatch is the historical effect of the large psychiatric hospitals; districts which used to run them still spend more on mental health care for their population (Exhibit 7). Such hospitals are usually located in rural or suburban areas with comparatively low needs. Inner cities, with their deprived populations and high needs, have 'exported' their problems in the past and some have relatively low mental health budgets as a result. Even though districts are no longer directly responsible for running hospitals, following the purchaser/provider separation and the allocation of funds according to population, the pattern of spending lingers on and is based more on history than on current need.

24. An adjustment to the current capitation formula for distributing resources to districts is needed since it does not make any separate provision for mental health needs. Suggested weightings for mental health resource allocation, derived from the most recent needs study (Ref. 13), would change the current (notional) funding allocation substantially. Some inner city districts, including London, Manchester, Liverpool and Newcastle, would gain by almost 20 per cent, while the losses in some rural and suburban districts would be more evenly spread and therefore smaller. A ministerial review of the weighted capitation formula is currently taking place.

Recommendation: The Government needs to reconsider its approach to resource allocation to districts to take special account of mental health, based on historical imbalances and population characteristics. Suggested weightings would lead to substantial increases in resources for a small number of inner city districts where many of the problems occur.

The use of resources within districts

25. Resources also need to be adjusted within districts. The needs of inner city sectors are likely to be considerably greater than those of suburban or rural sectors. Purchasers and providers should take such factors into account when allocating resources to different sectors within districts. Community teams, for example, will need to be larger in some areas than others.

A wide range of services is needed, including help with employment

Exhibit 8
The balance of hospital and community care

Most of the mental health budget continues to be spent on hospital care.

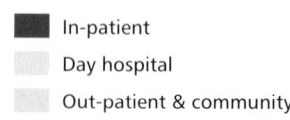
In-patient
Day hospital
Out-patient & community

Source: Audit Commission survey of local mental health services.

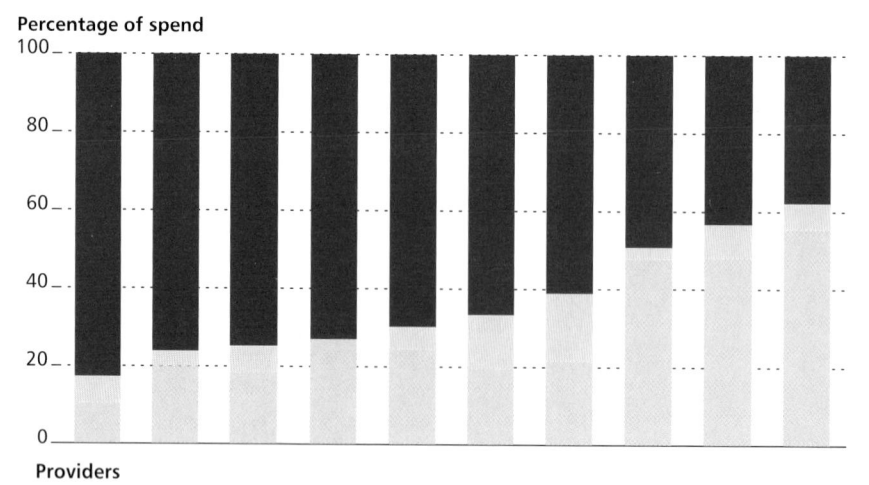

Percentage of spend

Providers

26. It is not just a matter of quantity. Resources should also be distributed in a different way, with a broader spread of community services available in many districts. Most of the mental health budget continues to be spent on hospital care (Exhibit 8), although the exact proportion varies.

27. This pattern has perpetuated despite changes in national policy. Community care is causing concern, not because the principle is wrong but because districts are finding it very difficult to implement. There is a marked reluctance to change the pattern of provision – often because it would be wrong to close beds before community services are in place. Where most of the resources are tied up in providing hospital beds it is difficult to break out of the vicious circle and to relieve the pressure on them (Exhibit 9). However, all authorities should be planning how they are to break this vicious circle. They should work out the mix of services needed, basing them on the needs of users and carers. The following chapters describe some ways to review the current use of services, which should enable some authorities to use their resources more effectively. Bridging money to assist the change can be a problem. Some purchasers have begun to set up development funds to 'pump-prime' new services.

Recommendation: Purchasers and providers should make use of all the available information on needs when allocating resources to different sectors within districts. This should include census data on deprivation, caseload registers, GP lists and information from housing agencies and voluntary sector providers.

Recommendation: Purchasers should assist in the development of community services, possibly through a 'pump-priming' fund. Purchasers and providers together, bearing in mind the wishes of users and carers, should work out the mix of services needed, aiming to meet the full range of individual needs while maintaining an adequate level of skilled professional care. The balance of provision by the different agencies should be expected to vary between districts.

Exhibit 9
The vicious circle

Where most of the resources are tied up providing hospital beds it is difficult to relieve the pressure on them.

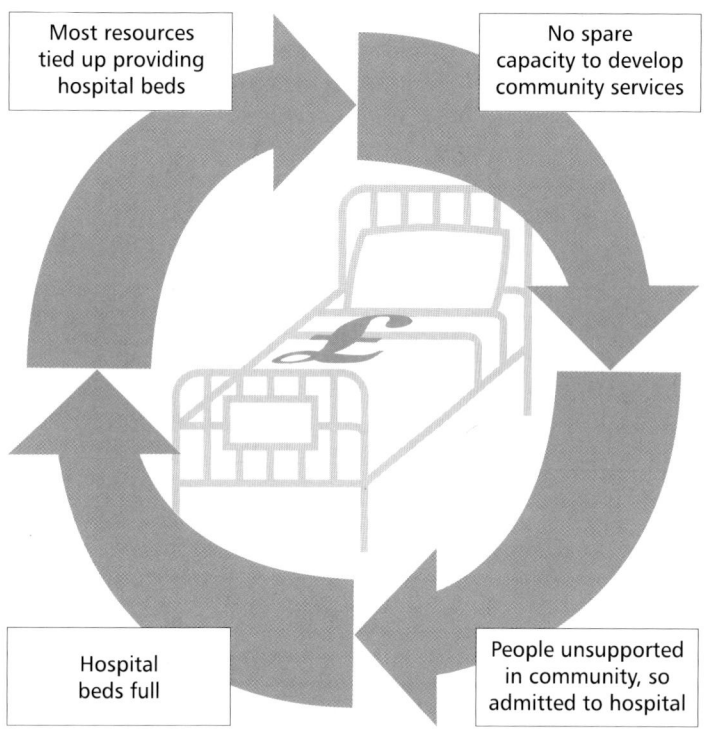

What do service users and carers want?

28. The past few years have seen an increasing recognition of the need to take account of the views of the people who use mental health services and of their families. Listening to users is important if professionals and service managers are to avoid falling into the trap of making assumptions on other peoples' behalf, since their views often differ widely from those of users (Refs. 28, 29). The Audit Commission has consulted ten local groups of users about priorities. A high degree of consistency was found with reports published by other user groups, including those which were produced as part of the Government's task force programme (Box 1, overleaf).

29. Families and other 'informal' carers provide a vast amount of support for people with mental health problems in the community. Very few of them, however, would prefer their relatives to stay longer in hospital (Ref. 30). They also want better community services which help to relieve the burden on them and acknowledge their important contribution (Box 2, overleaf).

A comprehensive local service

30. The needs of individuals span many different aspects of their lives so comprehensive assessment is essential. Poverty and inadequate housing are particularly common among people with mental health problems. Even though these matters are high priorities for users they are often overlooked by professionals who tend to focus on treatment and therapy. Good community services – which incorporate practical help and social care as well as treatment – can help people to stay out of hospital (Refs. 31, 32), so close working relationships between all the agencies involved in community care is vital.

Box 1
What do service users want?

Source: Audit Commission survey.

Better Information

The information given to people about treatment options available, the effects and side-effects of medication and the local facilities needs to be improved. People need better information about the range of services available. When they are admitted to hospital they should be helped to understand the rules and expectations, their rights and complaints procedures, their expected length of stay and the roles and responsibilities of hospital staff. Information in different languages is particularly important.

Rights and Respect

People want to be treated with respect and dignity, to have equality of access, to have access to advocacy and to negotiate treatment, and confidentiality. They want the right to a second opinion and to have any complaints dealt with in a proper manner.

More Appropriate Services

In hospital people want more opportunity to discuss and choose treatments, more privacy and safety, especially for women, access to user-only forums, better discharge plans and aftercare and for staff to listen more fully.

In the community people want more community supports and aftercare in general, more 24-hour crisis facilities and out-of-hours contact, the option of non-hospital crisis centres, crisis cards, more help with finding employment, more help with benefits and finances, and more support for carers. Sensitivity to ethnic and cultural needs is particularly important. Services run by voluntary groups or by users themselves are often the most highly valued.

More Education and Training

Service users need training in participation skills and advocacy. Professionals need training in understanding users' perspectives. GPs, housing workers and general advice workers need training in mental health issues. The general public need education to enhance their understanding.

Participation in Management and Better Collaboration

Users want more opportunities to be involved in decisions about their individual care and also in service management. Better collaboration and communication is needed across agencies, as is closer liaison with local interest groups, such as ethnic minority groups.

Most people with mental health problems live in the community, even those who have serious illnesses (Ref. 33).

31. It is widely accepted that a range of services is necessary to meet individual needs (Exhibit 10).

32. Within this framework priority should be given to people with serious or long-term problems who are at high risk of repeated admissions to hospital, homelessness or social problems if their community supports are inadequate. 'Rehabilitation' or support teams for people with long-term needs have been established in some districts. Some secure facilities will be needed to back up the hospital beds. Those who are less severely ill also need appropriate help but not necessarily from the specialist services.

Box 2
What do families and carers want?

◆ daytime occupation with flexible hours and a focus on employment skills;

◆ special support for 'revolving door' people – those who have experienced frequent readmissions to hospital;

◆ information about rights, services, welfare benefits, how to cope and how to complain, including 24-hour access;

◆ practical domiciliary help, including meals, cleaning, sitting services and personal support;

◆ respite care which enables carers to have breaks and which is agreeable to both the carer and the person cared for;

◆ a range of residential provision with different levels of staff support;

◆ practical and financial support for self-help schemes; and

◆ resettlement for homeless people and those in temporary accommodation or in prison.

Source: A forum of organisations: National Schizophrenia Fellowship, Richmond Fellowship, Manic Depression Fellowship and Alzheimers Disease Society.

Exhibit 10
The elements of an appropriate service

It is widely accepted that a range of services is necessary to meet individual needs.

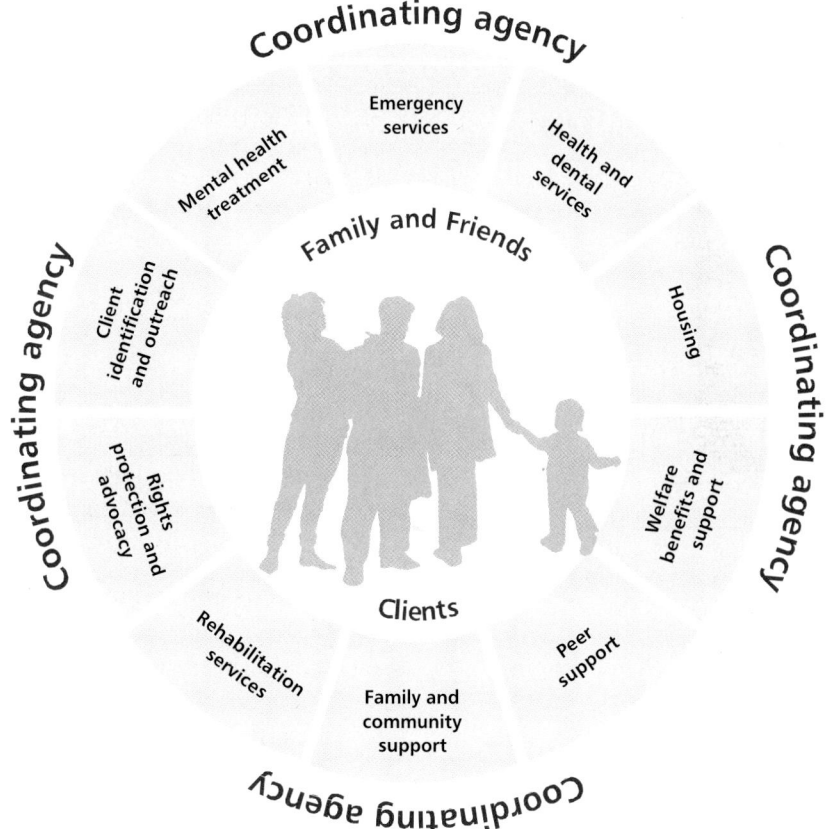

Source: Adapted from Turner - Crowson (Ref. 29).

17

33. Culturally-sensitive facilities for people from minority ethnic groups are important. Black and Asian people often find the standard facilities unsuitable, the food strange or inappropriate for them and there may be no one who understands their culture or their language.

34. Access to help outside of office hours is crucial since this is often when people feel most vulnerable. A rapid response to crisis is particularly valuable as admission to hospital can sometimes be avoided if suitable professional help and support are available.

35. A range of day facilities is necessary to meet the varied needs of different people and to enable them to take part in social activities and develop friendships. Having the opportunity to work is also very important for most people. Sometimes the best opportunities for real work are provided by the voluntary sector, although pressure to make ends meet often leads such schemes to select only the most able users.

36. Some of these kinds of support can substitute for each other. For instance, intensive home-based support can be provided for some people instead of staffed residential care, and home treatment can be an effective adjunct, and sometimes an alternative, to acute hospital care. Community support can be more cost-effective for some people. Information on unit costs is generally poor. Based on the data available in the districts visited the average weekly costs were:

Acute hospital ward	£616
Rehabilitation ward	£500
Long-stay ward	£369
Day hospital	£214
24-hour staffed housing	£340
Less-intensively staffed housing	£136

37. All districts should ensure that they have an appropriate mix of the elements of Exhibit 10, which will vary according to local circumstances. For example, sparsely-populated rural areas may require special services, such as travelling day care. Although some of these elements will not be purchased by districts they should be able to influence their development to some extent.

Alternatives to admission

38. Hospital admission for people with needs for acute care can sometimes be avoided altogether if adequate alternatives are provided. These can be more effective and preferred by users.

39. The best known alternative service is in Madison, Wisconsin in the United States (Ref. 35). People with serious mental illness received either hospital or community treatment for a period of fourteen months. The community treatment included 'training in community living' in peoples' homes and other local settings, help with employment, leisure activities and work with the family. The community group fared better in terms of psychiatric symptoms, employment, relationships and general satisfaction, although these advantages were only maintained for as long as the programme continued. The cost of treatment was similar for both groups (Ref. 36). The Wisconsin approach has been copied in many different countries, including Britain, almost always with the same results (Refs. 37 - 40)(Case Study 1).

40. Although it is not possible to do without hospital care altogether the use of hospital can be reduced by a combination of fewer admissions and shorter stays on each occasion. Relatively straightforward changes in the style of working, such as home-based assessments involving a psychiatrist and another professional within two weeks of referral for non-urgent cases and immediately if urgent, can make a great improvement to the effectiveness and efficiency of the service (Ref. 41).

41. So, a good service would be comprehensive, provide alternatives to admission and, above all, consult users and carers. In practice, however, an appropriate spread of community services is rarely available.

Case Study 1
Treating people at home

West Birmingham Home
Treatment Team

This service provides treatment at home for people with acute mental illness as an alternative to hospital care.

The team aims to prevent admission to hospital by providing alternative intervention and treatment in the community, recognising the overall needs of the individual rather than just the medical needs. Wherever possible the service avoids coercive interventions and treatment will be based on consent and agreement with the client.

The service is funded by the closure of hospital beds.

It is a district service, relating to several sectors with referrals through local community teams.

The team provides a service to an inner urban area with substantial minority ethnic communities who disliked the hospital-based service.

Fifteen people can be in the service at any one time. The service operates seven days a week, 9 a.m. to 9 p.m. with on-call cover from 9 p.m. to 9 a.m.

The team has negotiated the use of short-term crisis accommodation in the independent sector when people cannot be maintained in their own homes.

The team is committed in its operational policy to anti-oppressive practice, employs a substantial number of minority ethnic staff and provides a service which is welcomed by African-Caribbean and Asian clients.

Engagement is emphasised as a continuous process. Individuals may be visited three times a day and attention is given to practical matters, e.g., help with child care, budgeting to enable people to buy food etc.

The team liases closely with the CMHT and with social services.

The multidisciplinary team meets 3 times a week to review individuals and care plans are updated at least once a week.

Exhibit 11
Expenditure in three districts

The distribution of expenditure on
hospital beds and different kinds of
community services varies considerably.

Legend:
- CPNs + CMHTs
- 24hr staffed housing
- Community support - long-term needs
- Clinical psychology
- Employment schemes
- Day hospitals + day centres
- Hospital beds

Source: Audit Commission survey.

The current balance of resources

42. In most districts hospital beds still account for most of the mental health
expenditure (see Exhibit 8), although the proportion varies. The distribution
of expenditure on different kinds of community service also varies between
districts (Exhibit 11).

43. District B spends most of its resources on hospital beds. District A has
reduced its dependency on hospital provision and now spends most on
24-hour staffed housing. District C has a spread of expenditure across a range
of community services and fewer beds, even though the population is
comparatively more deprived with a higher Jarman 'under-privileged area'
score (Jarman scores: A = -17.32, B = -2.71, C = 3.02).

Exhibit 12
The range of services provided

Few districts provide the community
services which are most valued by users
(see Box 1, page 16)

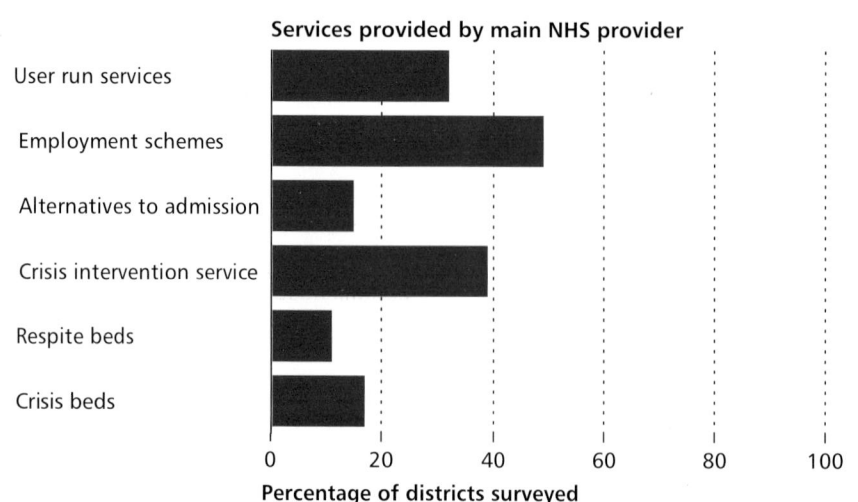

Source: Audit Commission survey.

Exhibit 13
**The pattern of sheltered housing
in two districts**

District F provides only 24-hour care
but District G has developed a range of
services.

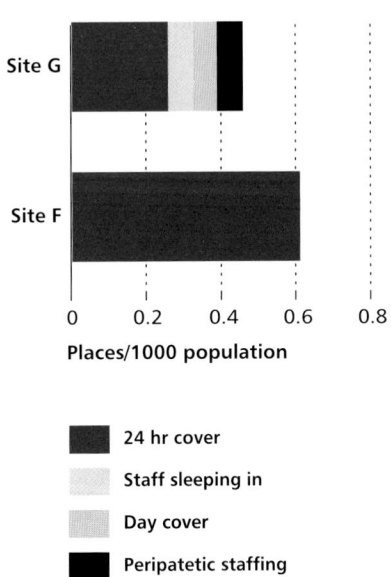

Places/1000 population

■ 24 hr cover

Staff sleeping in

Day cover

■ Peripatetic staffing

Source: Audit Commission survey, two districts.

44. The 'right' balance for any district will depend on local circumstances, such as needs, the existence of other providers and travelling distances. It is clear, however, that some districts provide a wider range of services than others within a similar budget, with less dependency on hospitals. Some included day, employment and supported housing options whereas others had little more than a community psychiatric nursing (CPN) team. Sometimes other agencies, such as social services, make a substantial contribution through day care and other local resources, changing the balance which the NHS needs to provide. So long as a mix of services is available it does not matter much which agency provides them. Only a few districts provide the services which are most highly valued by users (Exhibit 12). None of the districts surveyed had a complete range of community services.

45. Supported housing for people who need permanent or long-stay accommodation is an important element of service. It is also a particularly high cost area. Although some people need support 24 hours a day, for others a less intensive level of support is appropriate. Some districts provide only 24-hour care but others have developed a range of services (Exhibit 13; Case Study 2). In some places, high provision of staffed accommodation has emerged because priority has been given to finding jobs for staff displaced from the old long-stay hospital.

46. The balance of housing provision is considerably less costly in District G (Table 1, overleaf). District F could provide for 24 more people than it does at present, for the same cost, if the balance was the same as that in District G. Since F is less socially deprived it should be possible to change the balance of provision without too much difficulty. If all districts provided the same proportion of 24-hour staffed and less-intensively staffed places as District G (based on the national median of 11.1 places per 100,000, 77 per cent of them with 24-hour staffing) £40m would be released. This would fund a further 6,000 places at the average cost per place, including 14 per cent with 24-hour staffing.

Case Study 2
More effective use of resources

Salford Rehabilitation Service – supported
housing

This service is able to support more people than previously in community accommodation (as well as providing rehabilitation beds in hospital, thus freeing up acute beds by adjusting the level of staff support provided).

People resettled from long-stay hospital were initially placed in schemes with 24-hour staffing with waking night cover. As more experience was gained in managing supported housing it was possible to change the amount of support offered to the residents and in particular to replace resident waking night staff with peripatetic support.

In 1988 67 staff were supporting 50 people in the community and 12 in hospital.

In 1994 63.5 staff are supporting 89 people in the community and 23 in hospital.

Table 1

The cost of housing in two districts

The balance of provision is considerably less costly in District G.

	District F	District G
Population	287,000	220,000
Jarman score	-17.32 (well to do)	23.59 (deprived)
24-hour places	61	22
Less intensively staffed	-	24
Average weekly cost per place	£340	£234

Recommendation: Purchasers should review the balance of expenditure on hospital and community services, comparing their balance of resources with other districts and taking social deprivation factors into account. Both health and social services resources should be considered. The review should investigate the scope for the possible substitution of some hospital care with community alternatives, including both 24-hour staffed accommodation and less intensively staffed provision. The review should incorporate the measures of targeting which are outlined in the next chapter.

Recommendation: Providers should review their use of 24-hour staffed housing to determine whether it is adequate. The length of stay of residents should be reviewed and the intensity of support reduced where it is not justified by the levels of dependency. It may be possible to substitute sleep-in and on-call cover for waking night staff in some cases. It is usually more appropriate to change the level of support to people, while allowing them to remain in the same house, than expecting them to move elsewhere.

Skill mix

47. Many of the tasks carried out by community staff involve everyday skills, rather than the specialist skills unique to highly-trained mental health professionals – for example, accompanying people to the DSS benefits office or the housing department or helping them with household tasks. Unqualified workers – possibly neighbours or other interested individuals – can provide much of this help, if they are given support and supervision from professional workers. Users will need to be consulted if neighbours become involved, in case confidentiality should become a problem. Since the costs of employing these people are lower, more staff can be deployed for the same resources (Case Studies 3 and 4). Highly-trained professionals should only be used where their skills are really needed.

Case Study 3
Unqualified community support workers

Salford Social Services

This service provides appropriate help to a previously unserved group, to the greater satisfaction of users.

◆ The service seeks to provide support on a time-limited basis to people with long-term mental health problems living in the community by developing a network of support through ordinary community resources.

◆ The support workers are based in the most deprived areas of the Borough.

◆ They are funded by MISG and managed by Social Services with additional support provided by NHS staff (clinical psychology and occupational therapy).

◆ Goals are set with users in individual planning meetings attended by the user, the support worker and a qualified professional.

◆ Those recruited all had some experience of caring but not necessarily any professional qualifications. They were given ten weeks training and induction, leading to a tailored City and Guilds course at the local College of Further Education, attended by the workers and some service users. Inputs to the course were provided by health and social services professionals, representatives from the voluntary and private sectors and users and carers.

Case Study 4
Involving local people

Hackney Concerned Neighbour Scheme

This service provides extra back-up to people with severe, long-term mental health problems living in independent council housing, at very low cost and without a stigmatising mental health label.

◆ The scheme identified interested people through tenants' associations.

◆ Concerned neighbours keep an eye on people, perhaps popping in daily, cooking a meal, sharing a cup of tea, depending on individual need.

◆ Concerned neighbours receive £10.00 a week in expenses.

◆ If the neighbours are concerned and contact the support team, they are assured of an immediate response.

48. The hourly costs of a range of mental health professionals (excluding overheads, mid-point of scales) are as follows:

Nurses:	G grade	£22.83
	E grade	£17.31
	A grade	£6.75
Social workers		£19.13
OT seniors II		£18.14

49. More care could be made available to people in the community if a more appropriate mix of staff grades were employed. If 20 per cent of G grade CPNs were replaced with A grades (unqualified), £13m would be released, which could fund, for example, an extra 1,428 A grade posts, providing a further two million hours of care (or 633 G grade posts, or an appropriate combination of both).

50. The weekly costs of three different packages of care would be as follows:

1. Staffed accommodation (not 24-hour)
    Two hours CPN time
    One hour social work
    Total cost = £200

2. Staffed accommodation (not 24-hour)
    Five hours support worker time
    Total cost = £170

3   Staffed accommodation (not 24-hour)
    One day per week at a day hospital
    Total cost = £179

Package 2 provides the largest amount of support at the lowest cost.

Recommendation: Managers should review the skill mix of community professionals and consider employing unqualified staff, with support and suitable training for mental health work, for certain tasks. The roles of professionals such as CPNs should be more clearly defined.

---

51. This chapter has shown that there is a mismatch between the local needs for mental health care and the resources allocated to meet them. This is the case not only between districts but also within them. The spread of hospital and community resources is not sufficient to meet the needs identified by users and carers. In many districts the efficiency of the resources would be improved by substituting some less intensively staffed accommodation (which would make available an extra 6,000 places) and employing some less-highly qualified staff (which would make it possible to provide an extra two million hours of care).

Recommendations

Purchasers and provider managers together, bearing in mind the wishes of users and carers, should develop clear guidance on the appropriate balance of hospital and community services in the local area, with a definite timetable for its achievement. Good leadership skills will be needed.

1 The Government needs to reconsider its approach to resource allocation to districts to take special account of mental health, based on historical imbalances and population characteristics.

2 Purchasers and providers should make use of all the available information on needs, such as census data, caseload registers and GP lists, when allocating resources to different sectors within districts.

3 Purchasers should review the balance of expenditure on hospital and community resources, comparing their balance of resources with other districts and taking social deprivation factors into account. Both health and social services resources should be considered. The review should investigate the scope for the possible substitution of some hospital care with community alternatives, including both 24-hour staffed accommodation and less-intensively staffed provision. The review should incorporate the measures of targeting which are outlined in the next chapter.

4 Providers should review their use of 24-hour staffed housing to determine whether it is adequate. The intensity of support should be reduced where it is not justified by the levels of dependency.

5 Managers should review the skill mix of community professionals and consider employing unqualified staff, with support and suitable training for mental health work, for certain tasks.

2 Making Best Use of Resources

Resources are not well targeted to need.
Many community services do not serve people who are severely mentally ill.

Many hospitals do not target those with severe mental illness sufficiently; if they did, £100m could be made available for community services.

Services can be better managed.
Primary care should be better supported to take care of people with less severe mental illness.

The participation of users and carers should be encouraged.

The care programme approach should be implemented in all districts.

Community teams should have more effective management, with regular workload monitoring and clearer guidelines.

Professional guidance and training need to be improved.

Hospital and community services need to be fully integrated.

52. Having the right balance of resources is only part of the answer. Services must be used in the most effective way if they are to serve the people in greatest need. Those with severe or long-term mental illness are the most likely to 'fall through the cracks' if the service system is inadequate. New community services often overlook the needs of this group (Refs. 42 - 44).

53. This chapter looks at how effectively community and hospital services are targeted on people with the most serious problems and the steps required to improve the situation. For targeting to work properly primary care teams must be sufficiently funded, trained and supported to deal with 'less serious' mental health problems and the effectiveness of specialist community health teams must be improved. This involves the following elements, which will be addressed in this chapter:

- user and carer participation in key decisions;
- care programmes for individuals;
- better management of community professionals;
- improved professional skills; and
- hospital and community working together, managed in an effective manner.

Primary care

54. The provision of a sufficient range of appropriate resources, with well targeted community teams and hospitals, is not enough to provide comprehensive care unless they are coordinated with an effective primary care service, capable of dealing with the majority of lesser problems. GPs are usually the first point of contact and deal with most people satisfactorily in the primary care setting. However, they need the back-up and support of an effective mental health service if they are to cope; and they need adequate resources and training. They play a part in the support of people with long-term mental health problems, although their responsibilities are different from those of the specialist services. Primary care services have the advantage of not carrying the stigma of specialist mental health care. They are likely to be locally accessible and can provide continuity over a long period of time. They also have an important role in suicide prevention; most of the people who commit suicide have contacted their GP within the previous month (Ref. 45).

Care of people with less severe problems

55. The number of people with short-term problems such as mild depression and anxiety is too large for specialist mental health services to be able to deal with. On average there are 15 GPs to every psychiatrist and five to ten GPs to every CPN. Each GP might be expected to have 300-600 patients with mild depression and anxiety on their caseload in any one year as well as about seven with severe and long-term mental illness such as schizophrenia (Ref. 46). A typical CPN caseload (average 35) could be completely accounted for by those with severe illnesses. Any extension to include those with lesser (although often still significant) problems would reach only a fraction of this group and withdraw a vital service from some of those with serious problems (Ref. 47).

'Communication and understanding between specialist mental health services and GPs is far from ideal'

56. Communication and understanding between specialist mental health services and GPs is far from ideal as shown, for example, by the large number of referrals which turn out to be inappropriate (indicated by the caseloads of community teams – see below, 'Service Targeting'). GPs need to be fully informed about the criteria for acceptance by the specialist services and to have some alternatives in primary care for those who do not meet them (Case Study 5). There is a wide variation between GPs in their capacity to recognise and deal with mental illness; many problems are missed and, even when they do detect them, they often do not know how best to help. This stems partly from a lack of agreement over what should be handled in this setting and partly from a variation in training. An education programme, aimed at helping, is being coordinated throughout England by a network of GP tutors. Most GPs will need to be better funded and supported if they are to carry out their role effectively.

57. Primary care interventions can be very effective, as shown in a number of experimental schemes. Group training in interview techniques has been shown to improve GPs' detection of depression, the interventions they carried out – which became more specific and more focused on psycho-social problems – and patients' satisfaction with their care (Ref. 48). Brief educational programmes on depression and its treatment can greatly enhance the recognition and response to depressive problems by GPs, leading to a reduction in the rates of suicides and hospital admission (Ref. 49). GPs have also been successfully trained in brief therapies, such as problem solving and cognitive therapy (Ref. 50).

58. The involvement of other members of the primary care team is essential too. Most practice nurses see mental health work as part of their role but feel inadequately trained for it (Ref. 51). Health visitors and district nurses can also play an important part. Behavioural treatments and cognitive therapies by nurse therapists can also be effective for people with phobias and neurotic problems and are more cost-effective than treatment by the GP alone (Refs. 52, 53). Primary care teams can also link people into voluntary and self-help organisations to good effect (Ref. 54).

59. Counselling can be effective in treating specific groups of people, such as mothers with post-natal depression (Refs. 55, 56), but it is less effective when interventions are not closely specified and targeted to need. Most counsellors do not have specific training and many of the GPs who employ them do not know what qualifications they hold (Ref. 57). National guidance on the remit and training of counsellors in primary care would be helpful.

60. The attachment of CPNs to primary care teams has generated considerable debate. Although many CPNs enjoy this work, their effectiveness in helping people with anxiety and depression is questionable and they are likely to 'drift away' from those with serious or long-term problems, leaving the latter group unsupported (Ref. 58). A more useful role for specialist professionals such as CPNs is to train and supervise practice nurses and counsellors in specific interventions for people with less serious mental health problems, with prompt access to specialist care when needed (Case Study 5). However, specialist services may not have the capacity to do this work and primary care may not have the expertise or the time to respond.

Recommendation: Most mental health problems – the least severe ones – should be treated in the primary care setting. GPs and primary health care teams need to be better trained and funded to identify which problems can be treated by them and to carry out appropriate interventions. They need to be better supported by specialist mental health services. The professional bodies involved should jointly establish guidelines on the elements of care which should be provided in each setting. The educational bodies should ensure that adequate education about mental health is provided for GPs. FHSAs should provide funding for counsellors and other professionals, together with better guidance and clarification of respective responsibilities.

Care of people with more severe problems

61. GPs and the primary health care team also provide an essential part of the care for people with serious and long-term mental illness. While GPs have only a small number of people with severe mental illness on their lists – although those within Greater London or where a large hospital has closed may have more – these people require more intensive care for their physical and mental health. GPs generally prefer the mental health services to take the main responsibility for their mental health care (Ref. 59). A quarter of all of those with a diagnosis of schizophrenia receive care solely from their GP (Refs. 22, 60).

Case Study 5
Community teams responsive to GPs

Lyme Brook Mental Health Centre, Stoke-on-Trent

Note:
Population served: 74,000

This mental health service works alongside GPs to provide appropriate and acceptable support with clear communication about who is to be served by specialists and who by primary care.

◆ Extensive consultation was undertaken with GPs during the development of the community mental health teams.

◆ GPs have immediate access to the team through referrals to a professional on duty four mornings a week. Traditional out-patient clinics which work closely with the duty professional are also available.

◆ GPs are informed of the patient's attendance and then sent a copy of the assessment and decisions made at the clinical meeting.

◆ GPs are encouraged to ring the centre for advice and information.

◆ Two of the CPNs in the team have designated roles in secondary care to work with people with serious or long-term patients and two are responsible for primary care work, for which the GP retains medical responsibility.

◆ GPs were visited after one year to seek their views on how things had developed. They were generally very pleased with the service.

◆ Local sectors in the future are to be based on general practices to further improve liaison.

62. Closer collaboration between GPs and mental health services can be achieved through consultation and shared responsibility for care (Ref. 61). Both psychiatrists and GPs value the improved communication and understanding which is gained by closer involvement. GP attachment services can reduce the number of hospital admissions (Ref. 62). Some of the GPs involved in specific schemes have chosen to take responsibility for the long-term psychiatric care of their patients with the specialists providing back-up (Ref. 63). In practices where the strategy for improving care has been similar to that used in diabetic care, the quality of provision has improved (Ref. 64). One 'good practice' innovation has been the development of clinics for people with schizophrenia, initiated by a psychiatrist in a network of GP practices in conjunction with a practice nurse. The initial attendance rate at a structured clinic for monitoring peoples' physical and mental health was very high and all those involved felt it to be helpful. Attendance dropped off, however, possibly because the clinics were unnecessarily frequent. The GPs were able to take advantage of what they had learned and to apply the monitoring approach when people came to see them for other reasons.

63. Many other mental health professionals, such as psychologists, CPNs, social workers and psychotherapists, also work in general practice settings. Although GPs appreciate such 'attachments', and they can help to improve the long-term care for people with serious problems, the management of such workers needs to be carefully considered. Where they are attached to practices they are often distributed unevenly (Ref. 65) in a way which does not reflect the level of need in the population (Ref. 66). This may be exacerbated, rather than

Case Study 6
Effective working with a GP

This GP takes the main responsibility for the people with long-term and serious mental illness on her list, with minimal input from the specialist services.

- The GP is in regular contact with the eight or so people with serious mental illness on her caseload.

- The GP prescribes and reviews medication.

- She has a knowledge of the individual and their family.

- She is able to educate them about warning signs of relapse and intervene early – family or friends may make contact about this.

- The GP can, at times of vulnerability:

  – give longer appointments;

  – see the patient more frequently;

  – adjust medication;

  – suggest extra services, e.g., day care.

- She can contact specialist mental health services available for advice and back-up.

- The GP can call on a CPN or social worker for home visiting or practical assistance with housing etc.

remedied, by uneven expenditure on mental health by FHSAs. There is also the danger, unless their work is monitored and forms part of a local strategy (Ref. 58), of attached workers drifting into working with people with 'minor' depression and anxiety. A good model for collaborative work is illustrated by Case Study 6.

Recommendation: GPs should be encouraged to take responsibility for the people on their list with long-term needs for mental health care, while they are in a stable condition, provided that advice and assistance is available at times of vulnerability. GPs should participate in care programmes for these people and local CMHTs should provide support to enable them to do this. Specialist services should review the needs of these individuals at least annually.

Service targeting

Community teams

64. Multi-disciplinary community mental health teams (CMHTs) are now the focus of most local services (Exhibit 14). They ought to be the referral point through which GPs or other primary sources gain access to the specialist service and to psychiatrists. Liaison referrals from general hospitals could also come via this source. Hospital beds and other services such as residential care

---

Exhibit 14
The mental health service system

Community mental health teams should be the focal point of the service.

Primary care   Accident and emergency   Self

COMMUNITY MENTAL HEALTH TEAM

Day services   Hospital services   Housing and support   Specialist services eg rehab teams

---

Source: Adapted from Patmore and Weaver (Ref. 67).

Box 3
Mental health categories

A	Psychotic diagnosis, organic illness or injury AND previous compulsory admissions OR aggregate one-year stay in hospital in past five years OR three or more admissions in past five years
B	Psychotic diagnosis, organic illness or injury OR any previous admissions in past five years
C	No recorded psychotic diagnosis, organic illness or injury AND no record of hospital admissions

should be accessible through them. Teams should be clear about the level of need that requires secondary care. They should provide a brief assessment or screening for everyone referred to them. Where an individual's problems are relatively straightforward, they should be referred back to primary care or other local services, such as voluntary organisations, with appropriate advice. Because of this central role it is critical that CMHTs focus on the correct individuals and tasks.

65. The caseloads of community teams were analysed to see how effectively they use their time. People on the caseloads were classified into three groups, on the basis of diagnosis and history of service use: Group A are those with serious long-term mental health problems; group B are those with acute mental illnesses; group C contains those with minor or more transient problems as well as those with serious problems who have not experienced hospital care (Box 3). The caseloads of psychiatrists whose work was based substantially outside the team were excluded from the analysis. Some teams were found to give priority to people with severe problems but others work mainly with those who have lesser problems (Exhibit 15).

66. This lack of focus on those with severe problems is worrying. In districts where teams spend almost all of their time with people with lesser problems

Exhibit 15
Severe mental health problems as a percentage of the total CMHT caseload

Some teams give priority to people with severe problems but others work mainly with those who have lesser problems.

- A : Severe & long-term problems
- B : Severe mental illness
- C : Mainly without severe mental illness

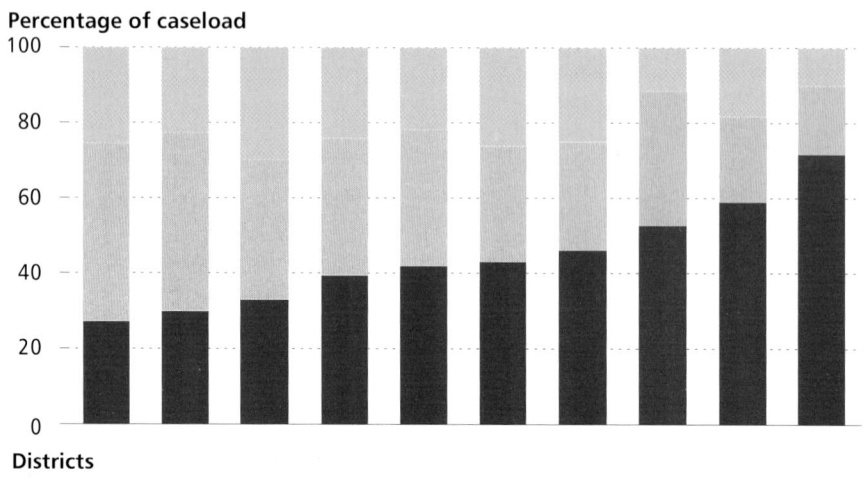

Percentage of caseload

Districts

Source: Audit Commission survey.

Exhibit 16
Caseloads in one district

The CPNs saw a lower proportion of people in category A than did the social workers.

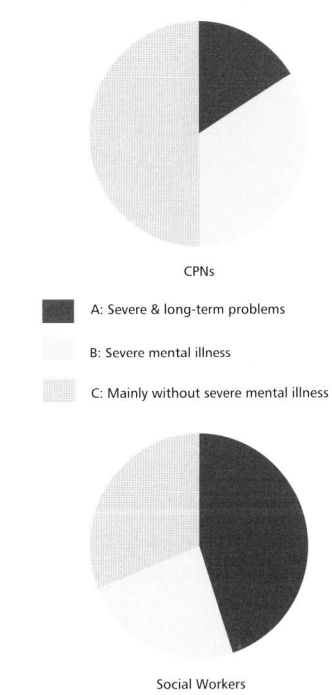

CPNs

- A: Severe & long-term problems
- B: Severe mental illness
- C: Mainly without severe mental illness

Social Workers

Source: Audit Commission survey.

many of those with severe mental illness and long-term problems may not be receiving a service. This greatly increases the chances of disasters such as the Christopher Clunis case. Even if nothing as dramatic as this occurs, many people with schizophrenia or other severe illnesses are not receiving the help that they need. If all teams focused their efforts on people with severe and long-term problems to the same extent as the top quarter in this sample, almost a fifth more people with serious mental illness could be provided with services and those already on the caseload could be provided with better care. In contrast (and as expected) the caseloads of specialist rehabilitation teams, established in some districts to support people with long-term problems, are entirely composed of people with severe mental illness (Audit Commission categories A and B).

67. The balance of cases held by different professions varied in many of the districts visited. In many districts the CPNs had a smaller proportion of people with severe mental illness on their caseloads than any other professional group, despite the profession having been created largely to help people with long-term mental illness. In one district the CPNs saw a lower proportion of people in category A than did the social workers (Exhibit 16). Nationally CPNs have shifted their working patterns away from those with severe problems, and a quarter of all CPNs do not have a single person with schizophrenia on their caseload (Refs. 68, 69). This implies that large numbers of people with schizophrenia, many of whom have severe problems, do not receive adequate community support.

68. It might be expected that professionals would work either with a small number of people with severe and long-term mental illness or a large number with lesser problems. No strong relationship was found, however. Those with large caseloads are sometimes responsible for a large number of people with severe problems (the top right hand corner of Exhibit 17) and others are responsible for a smaller number of people with less severe needs (the bottom

Exhibit 17
The percentage of people with severe or chronic problems on CPNs', social workers', OTs' and other therapists' caseloads

Those with large caseloads are frequently responsible for a high proportion of people with severe problems.

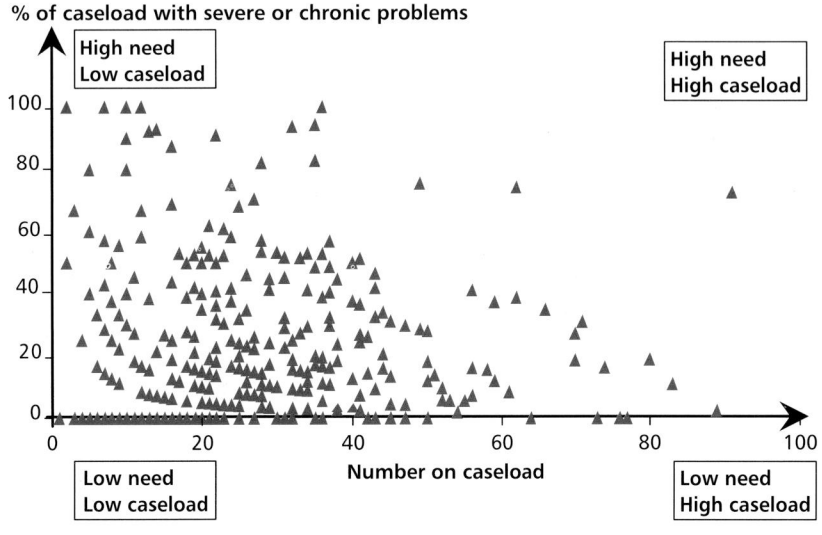

Source: Audit Commission survey.

Exhibit 18
The frequency of contact

People with long-term needs are not
necessarily seen more often than those with
lesser needs.

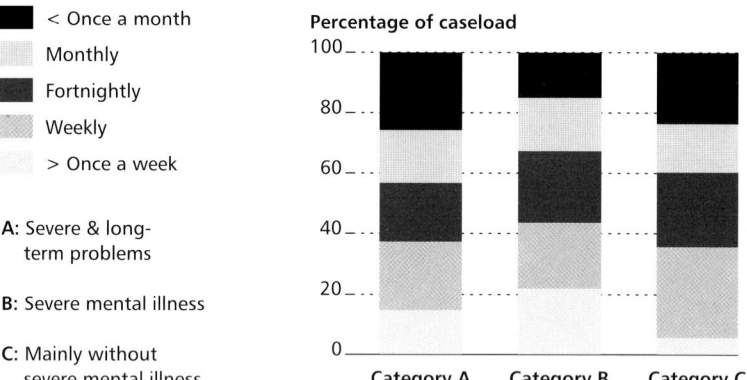

Source: Audit Commission survey, one district.

left hand corner of Exhibit 17). A rough guide to an appropriately balanced
caseload for a full time worker might be: up to ten with long-term mental
illness, around twenty with acute mental illness and perhaps three or four
without a clear mental illness.

69. People with severe or long-term needs are not necessarily seen any more
often than those with lesser needs (Exhibit 18), even though the extent of their
problems often means that they would benefit from frequent contact. Many of
them are seen only monthly or less which implies that they receive little more
than a regular injection. In many cases the reverse was true, people with less
severe needs were seen more often – although this might be appropriate for a
small number of them.

70. Nor does the length of time people remain on the caseload always match
their needs. Although most category A people are on the caseload for more
than a year, many of those with less serious problems also remain on the
caseload for long periods of time (Exhibit 19). Three months is an adequate
length of time for the type of intervention appropriate for most of these
problems. Spontaneous remission is also quite likely (Ref. 58).

Exhibit 19
Length of time on the caseload

Many people with less serious problems
remain on the caseload for long periods of
time.

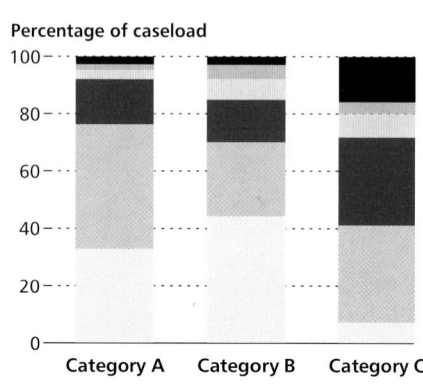

Source: Audit Commission survey, one district.

71. Many community professionals appear to be spending much of their time with people who have 'less serious' mental illness. Many prefer to work with this group, whom they believe to be more satisfying, while others may have been directed to do so by managers who have been inappropriately briefed. The main reasons for this imbalance appear to be inadequate or inappropriate management and workload monitoring, combined with a lack of suitable training for work with people who have long-term problems, addressed in the section 'Improving the Effectiveness of the Team'.

Recommendation: Community teams should focus on people with severe mental illness as a first priority and should work as part of an inter-agency group to develop the necessary local services. Clear criteria should be established and communicated to those involved in the referral process. Those with less serious mental illness also need effective care but this need not necessarily involve specialist teams.

Recommendation: Those with long-term problems should be seen regularly and on a continuing basis. Some means to ensure that priority is given to this group should be established, such as a rehabilitation team or designated workers within generic teams.

The use of hospital beds

72. The expenditure on acute beds was shown in Chapter 1 to vary widely and not necessarily in line with local need. The use of beds varies with both local needs and the admission criteria, which determine how closely the hospital is targeted to people with severe mental illness. The targeting of hospital beds also depends on the use of community alternatives by clinicians, particularly consultant psychiatrists.

73. The *proportion* of occupied bed days accounted for by people with a severe mental illness is a measure of how well targeted the in-patient service is to need and how consistently the criteria for admission are applied. If a service is very well managed and targeted, only the most severely ill people, such as those diagnosed as psychotic, are admitted to hospital and everyone else receives treatment in the community. A small number of less severely ill people are admitted for specific assessment or treatment but this should not vary greatly between districts. Using this measure the extent of use of hospitals for people with severe mental illness varies widely between districts and is unrelated to the level of deprivation (Exhibit 20, overleaf).

74. If all providers were to use their hospital beds consistently according to the same criteria as Districts A and E in Exhibit 20, the number of beds could be reduced by 12 per cent. If all providers in the sample used their beds according to the criteria employed by those in the middle, the district at the top would require a further 12 per cent while the district at the bottom would lose 30 per cent of its beds. On this basis £100m could be saved in hospitals in England and Wales for the development of community services.

Exhibit 20
Percentage of mental illness bed days used by people diagnosed as psychotic

The extent of use of hospital beds for people with severe mental illness varies widely between districts and is unrelated to deprivation.

* Jarman 8 Score

Source: Audit Commission survey.

Percentage of bed days occupied by people with psychotic diagnosis

| -19.29 | -17.32 | -6.72 | -6.38 | -1.09 | 2.38 | 3.02 | 9.51* |

← Low need ———————————————————————— High need →

Districts   A   B   C   D   E   F   G   H

75. The bed use in the geographical sectors of some districts varies (Exhibit 21). This is weakly related to deprivation but mainly indicates differences in the style and preferences of clinicians. Some are more likely to admit people to hospital but others prefer to treat them in community settings as far as possible. In Exhibit 21 sector one has a lower percentage of people with a psychotic diagnosis than sectors two or three, implying that the targeting of beds to those with severe mental illness is less effective in this sector. Although sectors two and three differ in their overall admission rate, implying that the needs are greater in sector three, the targeting of beds is consistent between these two sectors.

76. A low rate of readmissions to hospital is an indicator of how effectively the community service is supporting people after discharge – except for planned readmissions which are part of a specific care plan. The proportion readmitted over a six-month period varied twofold between the districts visited and was not related to deprivation (Exhibit 22).

Exhibit 21
Admissions from three local sectors

There is a difference in bed use between geographical sectors of the same district.

Source: Audit Commission survey.

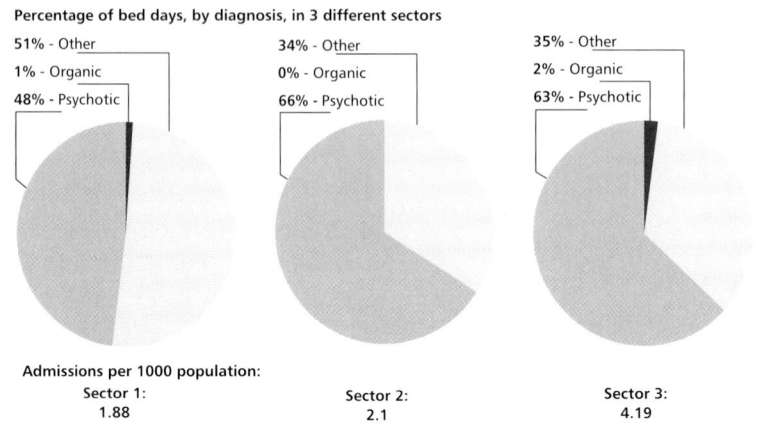

Percentage of bed days, by diagnosis, in 3 different sectors

51% - Other
1% - Organic
48% - Psychotic

34% - Other
0% - Organic
66% - Psychotic

35% - Other
2% - Organic
63% - Psychotic

Admissions per 1000 population:
Sector 1: 1.88
Sector 2: 2.1
Sector 3: 4.19

Exhibit 22
The percentage of people readmitted

The percentage readmitted within six months varied two-fold between districts and was not related to deprivation

* Jarman 8 Score

Source: *Audit Commission survey.*

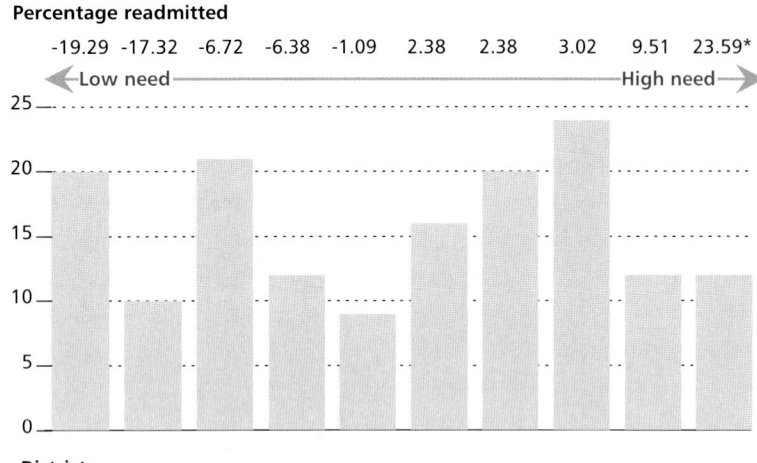

Percentage readmitted

| -19.29 | -17.32 | -6.72 | -6.38 | -1.09 | 2.38 | 2.38 | 3.02 | 9.51 | 23.59* |

← Low need ——————————————————— High need →

Districts

77. In some districts readmission rates were high, despite the availability of a good range of community facilities, indicating that admitting clinicians may not have been considering community alternatives first, nor using them instead of hospital. In such districts very few of the psychiatrists were involved in the work of community teams; they tended to operate from quite separate out-patient bases.

78. People are sometimes admitted to hospital inappropriately (Refs. 70, 71). In one research study more than two thirds of admissions could have been avoided had better community support been available. Other studies have found between a third and a half of those staying for several months on acute wards do not need such specialist care. Many have to stay because of lack of suitable accommodation in the community (Refs. 72 - 74). All of these findings point to real possibilities for reducing hospital care, which costs over £600 a week per place – provided that primary and secondary care are better balanced, alternatives are available in the community and hospital and community staff are better integrated. The cost of supported accommodation places will be more than offset by the savings in hospital places, releasing resources for community services.

79. Recent guidance on discharge (Ref. 75) has emphasised that people likely to cause a risk to the public should not be discharged until suitable arrangements are put in place. This could lead to further blocking of acute beds until satisfactory alternatives have been developed.

Recommendation: Hospital care should be reserved for those with the most serious problems. Criteria for admission should be openly agreed locally and clinicians should consider alternatives before admitting. The current use of beds by those with a severe mental illness should be reviewed and the possibility explored of reducing hospital care in order to develop more community services.

Recommendation: People should not have to stay for more than three months on an acute ward. Psychiatrists should be core members of multi-disciplinary (and ideally multi-agency) community teams as a matter of course.

Improving the effectiveness of the team

80. For people receiving specialist care it is essential that community mental health teams manage their work effectively. They need to :

◆ involve users and their carers fully;

◆ adopt a care programme approach;

◆ manage effectively, within a clear operational policy;

◆ deploy the right skills and ensure that suitable training is provided;

◆ work in conjunction with the hospital, ideally with some control over hospital beds; and

◆ plan and develop the services needed for severely mentally ill people.

User and carer participation

81. User participation is important for making the service system effective in meeting individual needs. Involving users in decisions can also help them to combat the low self-esteem and feelings of powerlessness that often accompany their experiences of treatment for mental health problems.

82. User participation is important at several levels of decision making. Individual care plans or care programmes should always involve the person on the receiving end (Case Study 7). This is a requirement of the care programme policy. At the facility level users may be involved in management committees of day or residential services. Some have user-only committees which can have a real say in decision making and control part of the budget. Users may also be involved in planning at higher levels of management, such as local joint planning teams.

Case Study 7
Users influencing their own care

Lewisham Social Services

This service enables users to make their own choices and state their priorities for care at a time when they are not under stress. In times of crisis professionals can make use of this information to provide a better service.

A 'crisis card' has been developed by Lewisham Social Services with the involvement of local users.

Individual users can choose to carry a card giving the name of someone whom they would trust to act as advocate, who can be contacted in an emergency.

The card also lists vital information, e.g., allergies to drugs, contact number for GP.

'Help sheets' give details of practical arrangements which may need to be made, e.g., child care, security of the person's home and bills that might need to be paid.

The use and effectiveness of the scheme is being evaluated.

83. Some of the main elements of good practice in user involvement are:

- resources, information and training for users to help them to get involved;
- equal access and opportunities;
- appropriate fora and structures for involvement;
- easily understood language;
- advocacy;
- paying people for their involvement;
- research and evaluation with results fed back to users.

84. The national networking agencies such as UKAN and MINDlink have a useful role to play in helping local groups become involved.

85. All but one of the twelve districts visited had a user forum of some kind and five provided some funding for user or advocacy groups. The small sums of money involved helped users groups to function. The impact of these groups on the development of services is not yet clear but the existence of independent, user-run groups is highly valued by their members.

Recommendation: Participation by users and carers should be given active support (including funding) at all levels and their views should have an impact on service developments. Training for users should be made available, in areas such as participation in and chairing of meetings, taking minutes and understanding professional jargon.

Coordination and care programmes

86. In the past, services have often been poorly coordinated. In one district users had to find their way through a maze of services on their own initiative. Care plans prepared by the CPNs or the CMHT did not include medication; day care was provided separately (although located in the same building as the CMHT); social support was provided by a separate rehabilitation team; and out-of-hours support was provided by yet another team.

87. The Care Programme Approach (CPA) was introduced in 1991 as a way of tackling this kind of situation. The principle is well accepted; a single plan is devised which sets out the contributions from each service and a single worker keeps in touch with the individual and makes sure that all of the necessary elements of care are delivered. The approach should be developed jointly between agencies and should dovetail with care management in social services.

88. Clear criteria should be established to define those who are entitled to receive a care programme and a register of people in receipt of care programmes should be developed with technical and clerical support to keep it up to date and remind key workers of review dates. The system needs to be monitored at intervals to see whether care programmes are being implemented as planned. Developing such a system costs money but major gains can be made for people with serious problems.

A single plan sets out the contributions from different services

Exhibit 23
The extent to which care programmes have been developed nationally

Implementation of the Care Programme Approach (CPA) has been patchy.

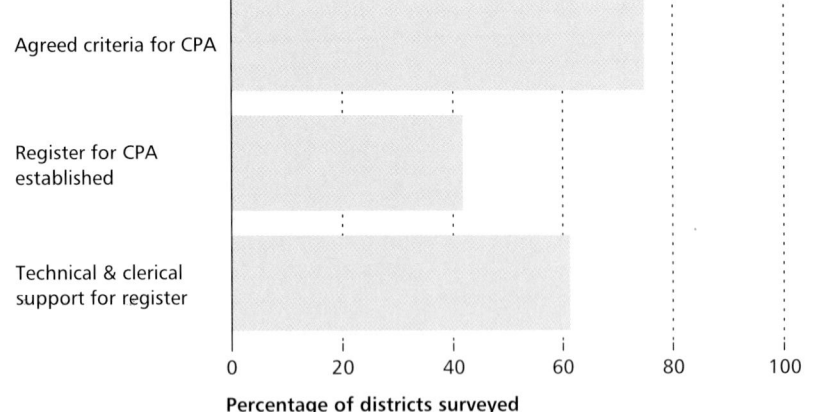

Source: Audit Commission survey.

Percentage of districts surveyed

89. Where care programmes are operating fully the coordination of care for vulnerable people has improved significantly. Users have said how much they value access to a named worker who knows them and can be contacted about their needs, regardless of which agency is involved (Ref. 76). In spite of these advantages the implementation of the CPA has been patchy (Exhibit 23). A quarter of the districts surveyed had not yet established criteria to define those who should receive a care programme and less than half had developed a register of the people involved.

90. The failure of many districts to implement CPA since its official introduction in 1991 gives cause for considerable concern, since community services cannot work effectively without good coordination.

91. In practice it is necessary to target the use of care programmes on those most in need, especially when setting up the Care Programme Approach locally, so definitive criteria for who should receive a care programme are essential. The number of people on the CPA register, however, varies widely and is not related to population size (Exhibit 24). It should correspond with the likely number of people with serious and long-term problems in the

Exhibit 24
The number of people on the CPA register

The number of people on the CPA register varies widely and is not related to population size.

Note:
The shaded area indicates the likely limits of an appropriately targeted list

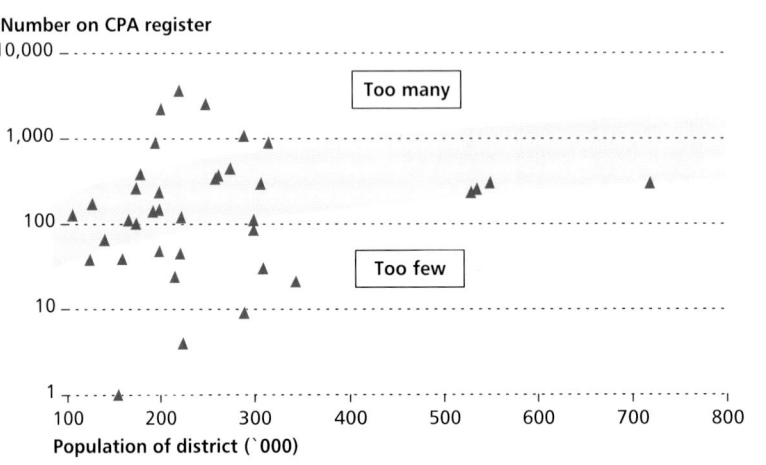

Source: Audit Commission survey.

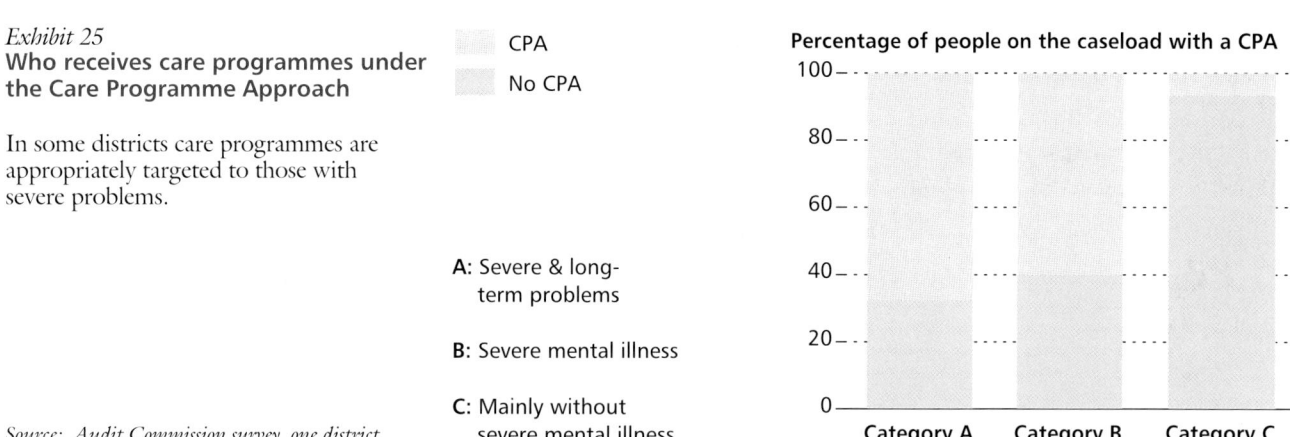

Exhibit 25
Who receives care programmes under the Care Programme Approach

In some districts care programmes are appropriately targeted to those with severe problems.

CPA

No CPA

A: Severe & long-term problems

B: Severe mental illness

C: Mainly without severe mental illness

Source: Audit Commission survey, one district.

Percentage of people on the caseload with a CPA

Category A   Category B   Category C

district. Those with extremely large numbers on the register would be unable to implement an effective care programme for all, nor would they need to. Those with very small numbers on the list have not yet fully established CPA in the district. In some districts, such as the one shown in Exhibit 25, care programmes are appropriately targeted to people who have severe mental health problems.

92. Care programme arrangements should be fully implemented in all districts. A written policy should outline the eligibility criteria – which should ensure all those with severe mental illness are included – and the procedures which need to be followed (Case Study 8, overleaf). For in-patients, planning should start as soon as possible after admission and the policy should set out who is to be involved in the process. This is likely to include the consultant psychiatrist, the key worker, other mental health workers involved in the care of the individual, social services personnel, the GP, the user and his or her carers. The involvement of social services is vital. The same requirements should apply to supervision registers, for a subset of people on the CPA, to ensure that they are implemented effectively.

Recommendation: All authorities should introduce a care programme approach in full, involving both health and social services with supporting documentation and procedures. Where implementation is very limited those with severe mental illness should be the first to receive care programmes.

The management of community services

93. Community mental health teams should be the first point of access into the specialist service, through which the other services are available, including the hospital beds.

94. Currently, much of the work of community teams is with people who do not have serious mental health problems, as demonstrated in 'Service Targeting'. Most teams are a loose coalition of independent professionals with freedom to decide what they do, when and with whom. To ensure that priority is given to people with serious problems, mainly those in categories A

Case Study 8
The Care Programme Approach in practice

Tameside and Glossop Mental Health Services

This service provides comprehensive assessments of individual need, clear responsibilities for coordination and regular monitoring to determine whether the care plans are carried out effectively.

All referrals to community teams receive an initial assessment (Level 1).

People with a psychotic diagnosis or considered to be in need of long-term support have a full assessment (Level 2) on which their care programme is based.

The same format is used for the social services care management assessment of people with mental health problems.

Each of the 12 dimensions of need is rated on a five-point scale for severity:

◆ the caring network;

◆ leisure and social network;

◆ emotional support;

◆ medication;

◆ symptoms and course of illness;

◆ employment / vocation;

◆ self-care;

◆ housekeeping;

◆ accommodation;

◆ finance;

◆ physical health; and

◆ safety.

A full assessment may take months but the most important areas are addressed quickly.

A copy of the care plan, based on the assessed needs, is made available to the user, the carers, the GP and the workers involved.

Services which would have been helpful if they had been available are noted.

The information system gives reminders for review dates and enables caseload monitoring.

Care coordinators from either the rehabilitation team or the locality teams take responsibility for assessments, reviews and liaison with other workers but key workers in each setting undertake much of the direct work.

and B (although some category C people will also have serious problems such as severe depression or phobias), community teams have to be managed properly and the different parts of the service integrated.

95. The teams provide a single point of referral for all sources. All referrals should be screened to determine whether they fulfil the criteria for acceptance onto the team's caseload and then undergo a complete needs assessment. Regular monitoring of the team members' caseloads is important for keeping them on track and providing feedback to the team. This might be best achieved by having a team manager who has the authority to allocate referrals and to monitor the work of individual staff, although no one model is likely to

A quick and appropriate response from a community crisis team can provide the help many people need

work in all areas. Additional clinical supervision can be provided by professional line managers where necessary. Alternatively, professionals report to a line manager from their own profession, which can be made to work if the strategic priorities of the team are very clear and such managers keep in close contact with each other. Consistency across different parts of the service should help. For example, the integration of out-patient clinics with the work of community teams should enable the same access route to be used for all admissions to community and hospital services. Clinical responsibility is held by the psychiatrist who should be an integral member of the team.

96. Crisis teams need to be managed with other community and hospital services if they are to target the people with the most serious problems. If the crisis team operates completely independently there is a danger of people entering hospital 'by the back door' and wards filling up with people who do not fit the target criteria. A quick and appropriate response from a community crisis team can provide the help many people need without having to admit them to hospital.

97. People with long-term needs deserve special priority for care and various arrangements have been devised. Some trusts provide a separate long-term (or 'rehab') team, which takes referrals from acute teams or specialist workers in acute teams. Many district-wide rehab teams experience boundary problems with the acute teams over negotiation of referrals and responsibilities, especially where the rehab team caseload is full. The likelihood of people missing out altogether is high under these circumstances. Other trusts employ specialist workers within acute teams for people with long-term needs. It is easier to maintain the special skills required for this kind of work if peer group support is available. Yet a third possibility is for the caseloads of generic workers to have a quota of people with long-term needs alongside others. None of these models provides the perfect answer; different approaches work better under different circumstances (e.g. Case Study 9, overleaf), so it may be necessary to adapt the model according to experience. The practices described in the case study operate in some, but not all, of the teams in the unit.

Recommendation: Community professionals should be properly managed and be given clear priorities and guidance. The management arrangements, ideally through a single team manager, should include caseload monitoring which distinguishes between those with more and less severe problems. A locally acceptable means of giving priority to people with long-term problems must be established.

Staff skills

98. If community professionals are to work effectively with people with severe mental illness they need appropriate guidance and training. At present there are no agreed national clinical standards or protocols for mental health work. Many professionals work completely independently, without guidance on how the balance of their time and activity should be spent.

99. Psychiatrists could benefit from good practice guidelines, to guide them in matters such as the prescribing of medication, frequency of review of long-term medication and working as an integral member of a multi-disciplinary

Case Study 9
Management to keep on target

Teamworking in the Pathfinder Unit,
Merton, Sutton and Wandsworth HA

This service provides clear management for its workers, guidelines on the balance of work which is appropriate and regular reviews of progress

♦ It is a sectorised service.

♦ It has integrated health and social services teams.

♦ There is a single point of access.

♦ It operates mainly via GP referral.

♦ There are regular meetings with GPs about patients to provide support and encourage appropriate referrals.

♦ There are mandatory reviews of all cases, using structured assessments.

♦ The caseload is classified into those with acute problems, people with long-term and severe problems, and people with long-term problems who are stable.

♦ Fifty per cent of work should be with those with severe, long-term problems; not more than ten per cent of the caseload should be people who are not identifiably mentally ill.

♦ All acute cases are reviewed at discharge or at the eighth contact if not discharged.

♦ People with long-term problems who are stable are referred back to their GP and reviewed by the mental health team once or twice a year.

♦ There are specialist workers in the team with small caseloads to work intensively with those with the most severe problems.

♦ Usable databases with brief details of individuals are being developed to enable monitoring of caseloads.

♦ The local social services department has taken the lead in providing a wide range of supported accommodation.

team, in order to improve the effectiveness of those who are least well informed about current good practice. The professional organisations and Royal Colleges could take a lead in this. Guidelines and protocols are also needed for other community-based professionals; a central core could be common to all professional groups, with additional specialist roles for each discipline. Quality assurance, incorporating clinical audit, is an important means through which to monitor the performance of professionals.

100. Training for psychiatrists should be based more in the community, in conjunction with other professions, in addition to gaining experience in in-patient care. The training for all groups should clarify which skills are common to all and which are unique to each profession. CPN training is not standard; although some have attended a post-registration clinical course, others have no special training in community care for people with long-term problems. Basic qualifying courses for all professions should be more focused on work in community settings with people who have severe mental illness. The Mental Health Nursing Review (Ref. 77) has recommended that all qualifying training should incorporate community-based work and that community psychiatric nursing should no longer be a specialty.

101. Many professionals believe that it is more satisfying to work with people who have short-term problems than with those who have long-term needs (Ref. 67, 68). This comes from a common perception that there is little that can be done for those with long-term problems. The experience of specialists in the area of long-term problems does not bear this out, however. A great deal can be done to help people to cope better with long-term mental illness and to enjoy a more satisfying life. A number of specific approaches have been developed to help individuals and their families (Case Study 10). One is to examine the patterns of interaction within a family, to classify them as either high or low on 'expressed emotion' (EE) and to assist them in finding ways to cope better (Refs. 78, 79). Another involves a multi-disciplinary team and engages the whole family in problem solving (Ref. 80). A third approach focuses on training the client, their family and professionals to recognise and respond rapidly to the early warning signs which nearly always occur during the period before someone relapses (Ref. 81) (Case Study 11, overleaf).

Case Study 10
Initiatives in nurse training

This training course teaches specific approaches which help individuals with severe mental illness and their families.

- The course is funded for three years by the Sir Jules Thorn Charitable Trust and is based in London and Manchester.

- It aims to equip nurses with the advanced knowledge and skills necessary for more effective work with people with serious mental illness.

- There are three modules:

    - problem-oriented case management;

    - family management; and

    - psychological interventions.

- It is taught by a multi-disciplinary team of practitioners and researchers.

- The interventions taught are those with a proven track record of reducing relapse and readmissions to hospital (Ref.82).

- Nurses will be trained over the three years and further funding will be sought. It is hoped the training will be made available to other professions (Ref.82). The total number of CPNs in England and Wales is 4,500.

- Other examples of training in work with families and psychological interventions include in-service training in Tameside and in-house courses in North Birmingham.

Case Study 11
Active intervention

North Birmingham Mental Health Services
NHS Trust (Ref. 81)

This service helps people with long-term mental illness to avoid relapse and involves them as active participants in their own treatment, using knowledge drawn from their previous experiences.

◆ The service targets about 200 highly vulnerable people with schizophrenia.

◆ It includes a focus on early warning signs of relapse and teaching self-management of symptoms.

◆ The individual and relatives are involved in identifying early warning signs.

◆ A simple rating scale is completed every week and intervention introduced to prevent relapse.

◆ Intervention is based on what has previously been useful, e.g., medication, day care, home visits.

◆ Evaluation of the service shows a dramatic reduction in relapse and admission in comparison with the previous two years.

◆ There is an active training programme to disseminate the skills throughout the trust.

102. The skills of community-based professionals in helping people with long-term needs can be extended by workers, such as specialist rehabilitation workers, teaching each other. A good example of this is training for ethnic sensitivity. Some services have recruited a number of black and Asian professionals. One of their most important tasks is to provide appropriate advice and training for the rest of the team (Case Study 12). Their role has to be managed carefully to enable them to take a balanced workload with opportunities for advancement and to avoid them having to take responsibility for all the ethnic issues and clients without adequate support. User involvement in training can help professionals to respond in more appropriate ways (Case Study 13).

Case Study 12
Acceptable and accessible services

The Maudsley Outreach Support Team
(MOST)

This service has managed to engage some of the most 'difficult' people with severe mental illness and to provide them with a service which they will accept.

◆ MOST was developed to reach people who find it difficult to engage with mental health services including:

   – those who refuse medication and fail to keep appointments;

   – those often brought in under a section of the Mental Health Act or by the police;

   – many with a diagnosis of schizophrenia.

◆ It is based in a deprived, inner city area with large minority ethnic groups.

◆ Many of the team are black.

◆ They work flexibly in people's homes and in local community settings.

◆ They have succeeded in keeping in touch with people who have previously refused mental health services.

◆ They have been able to intervene to avert crises.

Case Study 13
User involvement in training

Lewisham and Guy's Mental Health Trust

This service involves people on the receiving end of services in the development of the local service and its staff.

◆ User empowerment is one of the trust's objectives and is the responsibility of one of the directorate managers.

◆ Users are represented on the training strategy group.

◆ There is user involvement in every induction programme for new staff, including junior doctors.

◆ The trust is training users in selection and recruitment.

◆ Users are paid for their input.

◆ More experienced users involve less confident users in their training sessions.

103. Training is also necessary for work with those who have less severe mental illness, as outlined in the section, 'Primary Care'. Both primary care and specialist services need more appropriate training in suitable interventions for specific problems.

104. Community professionals also need to be trained in service planning, development, implementation and evaluation. Services need to be developed locally from an inter-agency strategic plan.

Recommendation: The training for mental health professionals should be more focused on work in the community and should cover specific approaches which are proven to help people with serious mental illness. Staff should be encouraged to share knowledge and skills, for example, in helping people from different ethnic and cultural backgrounds. Consideration should be given to the involvement of users in staff training.

Integrating hospital and community services

105. Hospitals should be managed as an integral part of the community service. Where hospital and community services are not communicating fully it is unlikely that the criteria to determine the most appropriate service (e.g., in terms of severe mental illness, vulnerability and risk) will be consistent. These are essential if community options are to be considered before anyone is admitted to hospital.

106. Psychiatrists are usually the main link between hospital and community services since their remit encompasses both and they are responsible for most of the decisions to admit. Psychiatrists should be members of both hospital and community teams and should be working increasingly in the community. Such links were present in only four of the twelve districts visited. Other professions can also be an important link where there are specific liaison arrangements but they tend to be based primarily in one side or the other. Community staff should work closely with the hospital when known individuals are admitted.

107. Readmissions to hospital can be reduced if frequent and flexible community support is available, as demonstrated by the service in Madison,

*'A single manager
with good leadership
skills should be
responsible for both
hospital and
community services'*

Wisconsin (Ref. 35). If the links between hospital and community services are weak, the chances of inappropriate admissions are greater. Case management projects in the United States have demonstrated the importance of links between hospital and community services for keeping people out of hospital. One case management team which was integrated with the hospital-based clinicians succeeded in reducing the number of readmissions. Another team, which was more integrated with community facilities but separated from clinical decision making helped people more with their social functioning but did not affect the number of readmissions (Ref. 83). Case management schemes in Britain, developed in conjunction with the Sainsbury Centre for Mental Health, helped to link people who had previously dropped out of care back into the service system. Their housing and social functioning improved in projects which focused on rehabilitation and their mental health improved in those which focused on treatment. None of them led to a reduction in hospital admissions, probably because they were not closely linked with the hospital service (Ref. 84).

108. Although avoidance of readmission is not the only measure of quality and effectiveness of a service, it is very important. Users prefer to have access to a range of options which can help them to avoid the trauma and disruption to their lives which often accompany admission. Carers and family members are often less stressed if their relative does not have to be admitted to hospital (Ref. 30).

109. One way to achieve greater local integration involves the provision of a comprehensive service to a local 'sector' with a population of around 50,000 (Case Study 14). Advocates for sectors have claimed that they make it easier to plan and deliver services and to control quality. A complete sector service would have one manager with full budgetary control over all services, including an identified number of hospital beds – providing a clear incentive to look for community alternatives before admitting someone to hospital. As such, they may provide the best mechanism available at present for inducing change. The social deprivation in different sectors can be compared using national census data to identify which have the greatest needs for mental health care.

110. However, sector-based services can have disadvantages if they are not used flexibly. Some GPs are unhappy with the way sector boundaries cut across their practice population. Sectors can also restrict choice; the quality of the specialist services can vary considerably and some GPs and users may prefer a different consultant and multi-disciplinary team – in step with developments elsewhere in the NHS. Sectors may also reduce equity; GPs may have patients living in different sectors, receiving services of a very different quality. A degree of flexibility at sector boundaries should make it possible to reduce these problems to some extent, with overlapping sectors allowing GPs to choose which service to use.

Case Study 14
A community-based sector service

Longbenton, Newcastle

This service provides all the main components of mental health care to a specified population.

A community-based, multi-disciplinary team providing for a sector of approximately 50,000 people:

◆ assertive outreach to people with long-term and severe problems;

◆ early intervention for people in acute mental health crisis;

◆ generic mental health services for a wide range of mental health problems, prioritising those with long-term and severe difficulties and including in-patient beds in a stand-alone, community-based unit.

The service includes:

◆ partial hospitalisation – 30-40 on list;

◆ in-patient beds – nine in single rooms with five back-up beds available in a hospital ward;

◆ both of these in a house in the community (the Grange).

Partial hospitalisation is flexible and includes evenings and weekends for those who need it. Others attend only for programmed activities. Partial hospitalisation provides acute psychiatric assessment, rehabilitation, support and social care.

The sector has 12 GP practices and 430-520 referrals per annum.

GPs are asked to prioritise referrals:

◆ emergency   to be seen within 24 hours;

◆ urgent   to be seen within 72 hours; and

◆ routine   to be seen within 14 days.

Previous service users may re-refer themselves.

There is a single referral point. All routine referrals go to a team allocation meeting where they are further prioritised, allocated for assessment and then presented at a review meeting. Some referrals are not picked up after assessment but are referred back to their GP with suggestions.

The CPA is in operation and all individuals taken on by the service are regularly reviewed.

The operational manager is line manager for all non-medical staff. They also have clinical professional supervision and multi-disciplinary peer supervision at review meetings.

It is not a 24-hour service but those in contact can telephone the Grange 24 hours, seven days a week. There is a crisis alert system; people who might need extra input out of hours can ring up and come in.

Some housing with day support is under development to prevent the Grange filling up with people who have nowhere appropriate to move on to.

Recommendation: Hospital and community services should be managed as an integrated system. Psychiatrists working in both settings should ensure consistency of criteria for acceptance into the service and should facilitate communication between them. The community mental health team should be the focal point for assessment, through which access to other local services is obtained.

50

111. Most of the problems described in this chapter are fairly well known and many of the proposed solutions are not new. Despite this, progress has been limited. The challenge is to enable real change to take place, which requires far more effective management than usually exists at present. A single manager with good leadership skills should be responsible for both hospital and community services. There should be a joint budget, to enable transfer of resources where appropriate. Purchasers must take a much firmer lead and set clearer targets for providers. Even with more effective management and accountability it is not enough for different parts of the health service to work together. The many different agencies involved in providing care for people with mental health needs must also cooperate closely, as described in the next chapter.

Recommendations

1 Most mental health problems – the least severe ones – should be treated in the primary care setting. GPs and primary health care teams need to be better trained and resourced to identify problems and to carry out appropriate interventions.

2 Provided that advice and assistance is available at times of vulnerability, GPs should be encouraged to take responsibility for the people on their list with long-term needs for mental health care. They should participate in care programme arrangements.

3 Community teams should focus on people with severe mental illness as a first priority and should work as part of an inter-agency group to develop the necessary local services. Clear criteria should be established and communicated to those involved in the referral process. Those with long-term problems should be seen regularly and on a continuing basis.

4 Hospital care should be reserved for those with the most serious problems. Criteria for admission should be openly agreed locally and clinicians should consider alternatives before admitting. The current use of beds by those with a severe mental illness should be reviewed and the possibility explored of reducing hospital care in order to develop more community services.

5 Psychiatrists should be core members of multi-disciplinary (and ideally multi-agency) community teams as a matter of course.

6 Participation by users and carers should be given active support at all levels and their views should have an impact on service developments.

7 All authorities should implement the care programme approach in full, involving both health and social services, with supporting documentation and procedures.

8 Community professionals should be properly managed and given clear priorities and guidance. The management arrangements, ideally through a single team manager, should include caseload monitoring, which distinguishes between those with severe and less severe problems. Priority should be given to people with long-term problems.

9 The training for mental health professionals should be more focused on work in the community and should cover specific approaches which are proven to help people with serious mental illness.

10 Hospital and community services should be managed as an integrated system. The community mental health team should be the focal point for assessment, through which access to other local services is obtained.

A strategic framework should be set in place.

Effective direction by commissioning authorities is a priority.

Able managers should be appointed to lead mental health services.

Local need assessment should be more systematic.

Strategic coordination is essential with primary care, social services, housing and the criminal justice system.

Careful financial management should be given to the closure of large hospitals and the resources retained for mental health.

Contracts and monitoring should reflect strategic priorities.

3 Purchasing Better Mental Health Services

112. The previous chapters have demonstrated that resources are not well allocated, not spent on the right mix of services and not targeted on the right people. These problems are primarily due to poor organisation and management. Mental health care requires services that are varied, responsive and flexible to the needs of people whose circumstances are constantly changing and who may be in only intermittent contact with them. It requires, above all, first class management and leadership, supported by good information (in addition to, but distinct from, sound clinical leadership). In the past there have rarely been the structures or inducements to attract good managers: community services have not had the same prestige as hospitals although they are probably more difficult to run. The NHS reforms provide an opportunity to correct this situation, with managers carefully selected and trained to coordinate the work of both hospitals and community services. Such managers will need to pull together the activities of the disparate, largely autonomous professional groups involved and the professionals will have to accept the overall direction of managers if progress is to be made. Managers, in turn, need effective direction by purchasing authorities as described in this chapter.

113. The requirements for a comprehensive service, outlined in the previous chapters, must all be drawn together at the strategic level (Exhibit 26). Strategic planning should determine the level and balance of resources, the priorities for those resources and the means of coordination between them. DHA purchasers should be developing their strategic role to a far greater extent, linking with primary care, social services, housing and the criminal justice system and setting contracts for providers. Few have sufficient experience and knowledge of mental health services at present to make key decisions with confidence. Such decisions tend to be left to the providers.

114. Even though information is the key to strategic management, the information available about mental health services is inadequate for both purchasers and providers in almost every district. Information is essential for the following activities:

- assessing needs;
- developing a strategy;
- coordination and joint purchasing;
- hospital closure and reprovision;
- contracting with providers; and
- monitoring performance.

Assessing needs

115. There are many potential sources of information on needs for mental health services; directors of public health, contracts managers, GPs and the FHSA, providers, local authorities (social services and housing), voluntary organisations, users and carers and the criminal justice system. However, these individuals and groups often work in isolation. Information is not shared and effort is duplicated. None of the twelve districts visited was making coordinated use of all of these sources of information. Epidemiological data and census data produced by the OPCS give an

Exhibit 26
Developing a strategy for mental health

The requirements for a comprehensive service, outlined in the previous chapters, must all be drawn together at the strategic level.

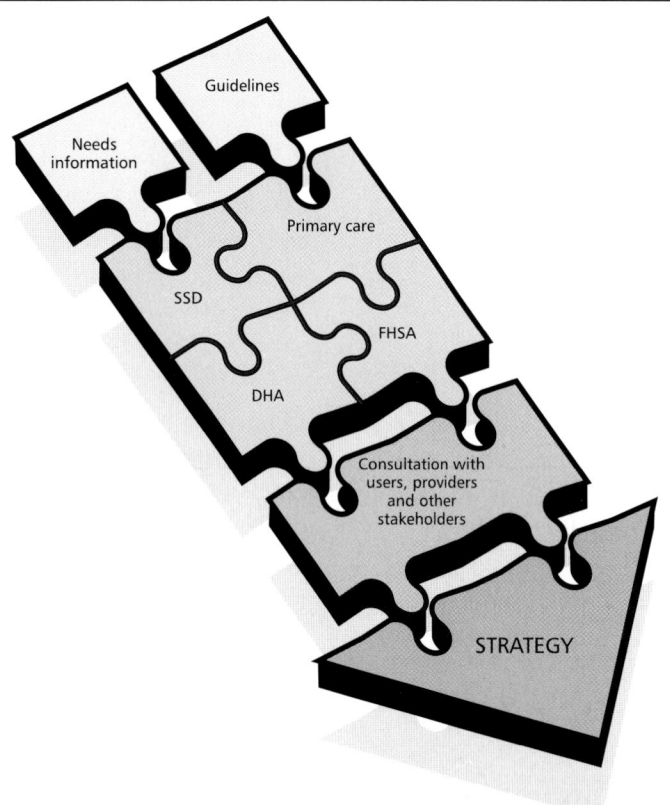

indication of the likely level of demand in an area. Purchasers should also require a local review of the people currently using local services to supplement their epidemiological data (Case Study 15). The numbers of people in the A, B and C categories defined in Chapter 2 should provide a start, followed by

Case Study 15
Identifying local users

The PACT team covers the Nunhead sector of Lambeth, Southwark and Lewisham and serves a population of 49,000.

This service carried out a systematic assessment of local need, using a variety of information sources, as one of its first actions.

◆ Print-outs from the local patient administration system were used to identify people with a diagnosis of severe mental illness and previous users of hospital services who lived in the sector.

◆ This was repeated for the GPs with large numbers of patients in the area and for the local specialist services such as forensic psychiatry.

◆ Further names were generated from social services, GPs, voluntary agencies, churches, housing and the police to develop a list of over 300 people.

◆ The needs of all these people were assessed and a register established based on the care programme approach. Advice was taken from users and others on the ethical, moral and practical ways of developing the register and its purpose was explained to the users. Only three individuals refused to have their names included.

◆ The register is now fairly stable and the team is using it to help to make the best use of the available resources by focusing on those most in need.

individual assessments of needs. GPs' lists can be a useful source of information (Ref. 46).

116. There can be benefits in maintaining a 'case register' of people with long-term needs as part of the CPA register in each district in order to keep in touch with individuals and to monitor service use, although this should be done with great sensitivity so that it is used to support users rather than to control them. There should be very clear guidance and tight criteria, agreed by clinicians and other interested parties, for inclusion on and discharge from the register, so that only those with continuing needs for support are involved. Access to information can be protected at different levels within a computerised system.

117. Different sectors within a district will have different levels of need, depending on their local characteristics. Purchasers and provider managers should review and adjust the levels of resources within different sectors accordingly, perhaps using epidemiological data.

Recommendations: Purchasers should make better use of all the potential sources of information on local needs, such as census data, FHSA lists, provider lists and other organisations. They should aim to know the number of people within their district needing long-term mental health care and to adjust the pattern of resources accordingly.

Developing strategies with others

118. Strategies should be negotiated by both purchasers and providers, taking account of other agencies such as social services and users and carers. In only four of the twelve districts visited so far had the purchaser taken a strong lead in developing clear strategic plans.

119. The strategy should identify the priority groups for receiving mental health care, the range of services to be provided and how the available resources should be allocated between them. It should take account of those provided by different agencies. The plan should give a clear picture of the balance of hospital and community services for the future. Targets should be set, such as the development of care programmes and timescales for reviews for individual users, and feedback should be given to staff on how far these targets have been achieved. The criteria for admission to hospital and community services should be explicit and consistent.

120. Within the boundaries of a clear strategy and priorities some local flexibility should be allowed in meeting needs, including some role in the practical and domestic needs of users. It should be up to providers to decide how to achieve this – for example, through devolved budgets, flexibility of staffing and the recruitment of generic support staff to undertake certain tasks. Devolving budgets to local sectors, which have a single point of management control over all community and hospital services, may be the best way to achieve an appropriate balance of services, although they will be limited initially, while many costs are fixed.

Recommendations: Purchasers should develop clear strategic plans, setting priorities, including defined need groups such as those with long-term problems. These should also include the balance of resources between hospital and different types of community service. Implementation of the CPA should be a requirement which forms the basis of the plans.

Coordinated purchasing: GPs and FHSAs

121. The main NHS providers cannot on their own provide a comprehensive service. Those responsible for social care, housing, education, leisure and work must also be involved and many health needs are best met by GPs and primary health care teams. However, only half of the FHSAs in the districts visited had both a specific policy for mental health and an officer with responsibility to promote it (Case Study 16). FHSA strategies are crucial in the development of services for people with 'minor' or short-term mental health problems. Funding and training for counsellors in primary care are important parts of a mental health strategy.

122. Good working relationships need to be established between mental health services and GPs to ensure that referrals are appropriate and that shared responsibilities for individuals dovetail effectively. Care programmes for individuals should help to clarify their respective roles. Misunderstandings between GPs and specialists are very common unless major efforts are made to keep GPs informed about the priorities and activities of the service. GP fundholders are particularly important since they control community budgets directly and may not share the priorities of the DHA. They are more likely to prioritise people with short-term needs since they see more of them, and they often prefer to employ a mental health professional themselves. This approach has its problems, however, since CPNs are a scarce resource and no one

---

Case study 16
Involving the FHSA

Cambridgeshire FHSA and Cambridge and Huntingdon DHAs

In this service a policy for mental health has been developed which clarifies the role of primary care and provides some support for it.

- ◆ Cambridgeshire FHSA and Cambridge and Huntingdon DHAs joined together as a health commission in April 1994 with both fundholding and non-fundholding GPs contributing to its planning processes.

- ◆ Prior to this GPs were encouraged to participate in local planning through a joint purchasing board of the FHSA and Huntingdon HA.

- ◆ The FHSA provides 70 per cent of the funding for counsellors in GP practices, including paid time for professional supervision. The policy for the employment of counsellors specifies the type of training they should have received (sufficient to entitle them to BAC accreditation), their accountability and relationship with the primary health care team, the expectations regarding confidentiality and record keeping, supervision arrangements and reimbursement. They are expected to provide mainly short-term counselling with some flexibility for the longer term.

- ◆ The activity of the counselling service is monitored by a local advisory group, which receives quarterly returns on the number of people counselled, the number of sessions completed and any onward referral.

practice has enough people with serious mental illness to justify their time. Users would also miss out on the range of skills available from a multi-disciplinary team. GP fundholders should be encouraged to give priority to people with severe mental illness and to participate in the mental health strategy.

123. At present GP fundholders purchase community mental health services but not hospital services. This could give a financial incentive to refer patients in crisis to hospital which is 'free'. If GP fundholders held the budget for hospital as well as community services, such a perverse incentive to admit people to hospital would be removed. They would be unlikely, however, to have the specialist knowledge and experience to purchase specialist mental health care for people with serious problems. They could purchase through the community mental health team who would put together a 'package', including hospital care where necessary.

Recommendation: Joint commissioning between DHAs and FHSAs should be encouraged. This should help them to develop coherent strategies with consistent priorities and to survey the views of GPs in a coordinated way. The DHA should work with GP fundholders to involve them in the mental health strategy and gain their commitment to it and its priorities. All GPs, including fundholders, should be involved in the local mental health strategy and should be involved in care programmes for the individuals on their lists.

Coordinated purchasing: social services

124. Social care is a large part of a service for people with mental health problems and joint working is the best way to provide it. Social workers are one of the most important groups of professionals providing mental health care for people with severe mental illness and care managers are responsible for purchasing social care for this group. The boundaries between health and social care are particularly blurred in mental health; sometimes one agency is the main provider, at other times the other.

125. The extent and nature of social services care is highly variable. Some local authorities provide only a small team of approved social workers (ASWs) with mental health training, whereas others provide a range of day and residential facilities as well as social workers in multi-disciplinary teams. Mental health care has traditionally been a low priority in many local authorities and the extent of provision is not related to local need. To break the vicious circle which keeps most of the resources in hospital beds, social care needs to be increased and, if local authorities are to provide this care, a transfer of funds between health and social services will be necessary. The mental illness specific grant (MISG) was introduced to address this issue but the amount is comparatively small (less than two per cent of the total budget) and the long-term future of the grant uncertain. The Government needs to reconsider how to apportion funds between health and social services for this client group.

126. Strategic agreement between social services and health is necessary to qualify for the special grant and essential for effective implementation of the CPA. It is also mandatory for the community care plan. Agreements on care

'Mental health care has traditionally been a low priority in many local authorities and the extent of provision is not related to local need'

management and the spending of the mental health portion of the special transitional grant (STG) to social services, which is based on transferred social security money, are also highly desirable. Some authorities have established effective joint procedures for care programmes and care management but others have encountered major problems in this area. Integrated community teams of health and social services professionals are very important. In the best examples of joint working the health and social services budgets are planned as if they were one. Conversely, tensions over finance can undermine joint working. Team leaders can be employed by either authority with some workers jointly funded. Local agreement over the respective roles of health and social services is essential, since there is a high degree of inter-dependency. Joint need assessments are a very useful way to promote cooperation and the sharing of work.

127. Some authorities have divided their catchment areas in ways that correspond with those of their opposite number. Sometimes the local authority has altered its sector boundaries to fit in with the health authority; in other cases it has been the other way round. More often the boundaries are not coterminous, which complicates the relationship between them.

Recommendation: The procedures for care management and care programmes should be developed jointly between health and social services and should dovetail together. Purchasers should set out the strategy and providers should develop the operational details.

Recommendation: Strategic developments should involve health and social services agencies working together with locally-defined roles for each. Reviews of the balance of local provision should include both health and social services resources. Sanctions should be available if either party fails to discharge its responsibilities. Geographical boundaries should match as far as possible.

Recommendation: The Government needs to work out the appropriate balance between health and social care and reconsider how to apportion funds between them.

Collaboration with housing agencies

128. Housing is identified by users as one of the highest priorities, yet housing authorities rarely recognise the significance of their role in mental health. Over 400,000 people were accepted as homeless by local authorities in England in 1991. Mental illness is much more common among homeless people than in the ordinary population, as noted in Chapter 1 (Refs. 85, 86). Mentally ill people are much more likely to become homeless, due to the breakdown of family relationships, difficulty in maintaining a tenancy or holding down a job or difficulty in claiming benefits and hostile reactions from neighbours, landlords or friends (Ref. 87). Suitable accommodation is in short supply so while some are homeless or inappropriately housed, others are blocking hospital beds (Refs. 72 - 74).

129. The closure of the old hospitals is not the principal cause of the large numbers of mentally ill people who are homeless. Very few of them have spent more than a year in hospital, thus refuting the notion that large numbers of homeless and visibly mentally ill people have simply been 'tipped out' onto the streets. For previous long-stay residents of institutions the reprovision of accommodation is generally considered good (Ref. 88).

130. Long-term or permanent housing is the goal for most people since frequent moves between temporary placements are very disruptive. It is better to adjust the level of staff support when necessary than to make people move on as their needs change. Users generally prefer small, individualised settings that enable privacy and autonomy rather than specialist residential care (Ref. 89). Housing for people with mental health problems can be provided by a variety of agencies. In some areas local agreements have been established with the local authority housing department to provide a quota of places each year, on condition that the mental health services provide support. Housing can also be provided through joint schemes which involve health, social services, housing associations and voluntary organisations. There can be occasional problems with the legality of complex schemes, where they involve trusts or health authorities combined with social security benefits or the STG.

Recommendations: Housing for people with mental health problems should be made available by local authority or housing associations, the living costs funded through the normal channels of social security benefits and the care provided, or at least funded, through health and social services. A national lead should be taken by the Departments of Health and the Environment together to provide more suitable housing for people with mental health problems. Local authority housing departments should also be working closely on this issue.

*Long-term or permanent housing, with flexible
staff support, is the goal for most people*

Collaboration with criminal justice agencies

131. Mental health problems are common among petty offenders, most of whom receive only short custodial sentences. These people need a more appropriate response to their problems than the criminal justice system is able to provide.

132. Although only a few mentally ill people commit serious offences, the needs of this group are not met adequately either. The Ritchie report on the care and treatment of Christopher Clunis was critical of the police and the Crown Prosecution Service. Their inaction, perhaps in a mistaken attempt to be kind, led to a failure to provide him with appropriate care. The communication between the criminal justice system and care agencies was ineffective and unhelpful (Ref. 9).

133. Current national policy states that mentally disordered offenders needing treatment and care should receive it from health and social services agencies rather than the penal system (Ref. 90). The Reed committee, which was set up to review provision for mentally disordered offenders, made 276 recommendations for the implementation of a more appropriate service (Ref. 91). People who appear to be suffering from mental illness can be diverted at a number of stages in the justice process, from the police, a magistrates' court or directly from prison to hospital (Case Study 17). The care programme approach, which should be jointly developed by health and social services, also applies to those leaving prison (Case Study 18, overleaf).

134. More than 50 diversion schemes, in which a mental health professional attends court regularly to assess individuals and advise, have been established at magistrates' courts in England and Wales (Ref. 92). These schemes have led to a significant reduction in the time spent in custody, sometimes

---

Case Study 17
East Dorset Community Forensic Team

This service takes responsibility for people diverted from the courts and provides a mental health service which is tailored to their needs.

People coming before the court are referred to the community forensic team which can:

♦ provide multi-disciplinary assessment before sentencing;

♦ enable people to get bail;

♦ take statutory responsibility;

♦ provide psychiatric and behavioural therapy;

♦ protect the public;

♦ provide a focus for people returning from special hospitals / prisons / secure units; and

♦ act as a vehicle for the development of other resources.

There is probation and health service involvement in the scheme.

Protocols for inter-agency working prevent problems around confidentiality.

A bail accommodation scheme has been developed with a housing association.

A probation officer was employed by the purchaser to develop the scheme.

The team also deals with sex offenders

Case Study 18
Prison to community

The Wessex Project

This service provides assessment and care planning for people with mental health problems who are leaving prison.

♦ The Wessex project is an experimental project set up with Mental Health Foundation funding to support the release of prisoners back into the Hampshire area by integrating them into appropriate local services through the use of the care programme approach.

♦ The team consists of seconded workers from the collaborating agencies: a psychiatric nurse, a social worker and a probation officer. Prison staff also assist.

♦ Any prisoner giving cause for concern regarding mental health problems is interviewed; those with indicators of mental disorder are offered follow-up assessments and those suitable for the care programme approach are identified. In the first year all newly sentenced prisoners received into HMP Winchester were screened for mental disorder. Screening of remand prisoners will be the next stage.

♦ Referrals are encouraged from any member of the prison staff and from professional workers in the community.

♦ The project aims to secure access to community services for prisoners with mental health problems as part of a coordinated response to their needs on release.

approximately double the increased admission time to hospital. The additional direct costs of the scheme are generally small and most of those given psychiatric help have gained some noticeable benefit (Ref. 93). The effect of diversion schemes is to decrease the use of prison resources and to increase the use of NHS and social services resources. Between 70-80 per cent of individuals are diverted to general mental health services rather than forensic services. As such schemes become more widespread the question of the transfer of funds between the Home Office and the NHS to match the responsibilities becomes more pressing. The resources required will include case management, highly supported accommodation, rehabilitation and work facilities.

Recommendation: Planning for the care of mentally disordered offenders should involve all of the agencies working together and should consider the resource implications of diversion schemes and transfers from custody. An adequate infrastructure of service to meet the needs of people who have been diverted is essential. Discussion between the Department of Health and the Home Office over funding is necessary at a national level.

Recommendation: Local purchasing decisions should be based on consultation with the other major agencies in mental health in order to make the best use of resources. These include health providers, social services, housing, the criminal justice system, providers of employment and education services, as well as a range of interest groups, such as voluntary organisations and representatives of users and carers.

Hospital closure and reprovision

135. Government policy is to close all of the targeted large psychiatric hospitals but progress to date has been limited. Most of the hospitals are still open, albeit with fewer beds and very high average costs per place, often in increasingly dilapidated conditions. It is possible to provide better accommodation and care outside of hospital without any increase in cost, if it has been planned around the needs of individuals (Ref. 94). Plans for the replacement of hospitals should involve all agencies. It is important to plan for a change in the culture of the service, to enable the ex-residents to live in a situation which is as close as possible to an ordinary life in the community. It may be appropriate to transfer resources to social services or other agencies in order to achieve this.

136. Six of the districts visited had old psychiatric hospitals still open. Most had a proposed date for closure but few had a clear plan of action, with a timetable of key dates, agreement on the financial arrangements and details of how individuals were to be resettled. Plans should include provision for day activity, employment, leisure and social opportunities as well as accommodation. In some cases there have been disputes over the financial arrangements with disagreement about how resources released by the closure are to be spent. In one district this had led to a prolonged dispute with social services.

137. The DHAs that purchase the bulk of the services may manage the closure directly or may delegate responsibility to the main provider agency. Even if not closely involved the DHA should demand a clear strategy from the provider which fits within an overall plan for adult mental health services. Negotiation between purchaser and provider will always be necessary. In Wales the Welsh Office has taken an active role in planning for the reprovision of old psychiatric hospitals. It makes the major decisions about the spending of any bridging finance and can veto plans which do not meet with its approval.

138. Finance must be carefully planned to ensure an adequate service in the future. Resources may have been gradually 'leaking' from mental health budgets into other health specialties (Ref. 95). This is difficult to trace because the definition of budget heads tends to change every few years. For example, services for elderly people with dementia have sometimes been included in the mental health budget and sometimes recorded separately. Some providers have used all the resources released for new hospital services, mainly for elderly people, in effect shifting resources away from mental health care for younger adults. To avoid such biases the responsibility for closing a hospital needs to be vested in a manager who has control of the total budget, including the mental health share of support services such as catering, and who can ensure that resources do not 'leak' out of the mental health budget (Case Study 19, overleaf).

139. Some of the closures and reprovision developments have been extensively evaluated. One of the largest of these evaluations, carried out in the North East Thames Region, has found the outcomes for most individuals to be very good. The costs of care in the new settings in the first few years have been less

Case Study 19
Retaining resources

Closure of Mapperley Hospital,
Nottingham

The closure of this hospital enabled the development of a range of community resources by maintaining a priority on adult mental health services, especially those with long-term needs.

◆ Long-stay residents were resettled.

◆ Acute care was reprovided in the DGH (and is planned at sector bases).

◆ All of the revenue which previously supported the 'old-long-stay' residents has been retained and reused to provide an extensive rehabilitation service.

◆ The budget is higher than most rehabilitation services (39 per cent of the total revenue for mental health) and is able to support a large number of people with long-term needs in community settings, both those resettled from hospital and people with long-term needs in the community.

◆ A range of housing options is available, with peripatetic staff support, as well as care management, home support and employment opportunities.

than those of hospital care, although they have risen as successive groups have been resettled from hospital. The overall costs have not risen significantly as resettled individuals have grown older, although they tend to make more use of hospital care (Refs. 96, 97). For most people community care is still less expensive than hospital care, partly because hospital costs have risen steeply at the same time. Bridging finance continues to be a problem for reprovision schemes since community services need to be put in place before hospitals are closed. This may need to addressed at a national level.

Recommendations: Purchasers should have a clear plan of action for hospital closure, which should include a timetable of key dates, agreement on the financial arrangements and identification of the responsibilities for individuals who need to be resettled. Any resources released should be identified and retained for mental health.

Contracting

140. Purchasers' plans should be translated into clear contracts. Contract specifications should cover:

◆ the nature and level of services to be provided;

◆ the prices to be paid for these services and the mechanisms for payment;

◆ the duration of the contract;

◆ the facilities to be employed;

◆ quality measures;

◆ the means by which the contract is to be monitored;

141. Contracts should be detailed and specific about priorities and policies and should specify locally-acceptable definitions of the 'health' role.

142. These should fit within the framework of the purchaser's strategic plan. The purchaser is more likely to be able to bring about changes in services by setting out a medium-term view (covering three to five years) in its purchasing plan, within which its providers can develop their services. A collaborative style of working is likely to be more productive than a confrontational approach, since the services contracted cannot yet be very tightly specified and

there is a need for flexibility. Factors such as quality, reliability, approach and convenience are as important as price. The purchasing plan should be clear about expected changes in the pattern and volume of services and in expenditure (e.g., more community services and fewer hospital beds, closer integration between psychiatrists and community mental health teams). It should signal longer-term plans to providers, so that they can plan staff development and plan investment. It should also clarify priorities for services and client groups.

143. Many purchasers are contracting with an increasing number of providers. Purchasers should develop relationships with independent sector providers, such as voluntary organisations, as well as with their main NHS provider. Some voluntary organisations have real problems with purchasers who try to use their buying power to negotiate prices at the level of marginal costs. They are then unable to fund overheads and developments properly which could have a serious impact on the quality and continuity of services.

144. Another important area, particularly in financial terms, is the use of beds in private hospitals specialising in caring for people with challenging behaviour. The prices can be extremely high. The number of people requiring such care in the district may be very small and this option may then be the most cost-effective. However, use of these beds may also reflect shortcomings in local services, perhaps in their ability to cope with more serious mental health problems or in the availability of secure hospital beds. Some local services should be able to develop better care locally for the same cost.

Recommendation: Purchasers should work with providers to develop detailed and specific contracts which specify short, medium and long-term targets.

Monitoring performance

145. The monitoring of mental health service providers is hampered by the scarcity of information about service activities and an almost complete absence of information about outcomes. The number of service contacts, which is often recorded, reveals nothing about the type of needs that are being met nor the type or level of service provided. Only two of the twelve districts visited had systems which recorded any meaningful information about community services, such as the number of people with severe mental illness on the caseloads of community teams, and neither of these was able to provide everything requested.

146. The collection and use of relatively simple information about caseloads, broad diagnostic groups, history of readmissions and frequency of contact can make a vast improvement to current practices. The evidence set out in Chapter 2 illustrates how this information can be used. These data give a better picture of the local service and the needs it is meeting than most of the existing data on finished consultant episodes or the number of community contacts (Case Study 20, overleaf).

Case Study 20
Service information

Tameside and Glossop community
mental health services information
system.

This information system enables the activities of the service and the progress of individuals to be monitored.

Details of all people accessing the mental health service are recorded on a computer database with basic identification details, diagnosis and assessment summary, workers involved and review details.

Reports can show by sector:

♦ caseload;

♦ case mix;

♦ service utilisation;

♦ outcomes (change in the severity matrix measured at initial assessment and review /discharge);

♦ ethnicity information; and

♦ services needed but not available.

Scoring from the assessment matrix could be used to generate charging information.

147. The monitoring of care programmes is a good place to start, since registers of people in receipt of CPA are a policy requirement. Although the numbers of people with a care programme will have to be limited, all those with severe and long-term problems should be included. Supervision registers, which should supplement the CPA, are intended for those most at risk of harming themselves or others. This group should receive particular care and follow-up. The monitoring approach may later be extended to other groups of service users. Team managers should collect information about the caseloads carried by professionals and the frequency and types of intervention carried out. Health and social services need to be agreed about their respective responsibilities and the sanctions imposed if one party fails to deliver.

148. It is important to feed information back to staff as well as to those responsible for planning and purchasing the service. A good information system should identify the kinds of needs being met and the gaps which future service development should aim to meet. Staff should find the information useful as a check on whether they are reaching their target groups and responding appropriately. Monitoring should also cover the quality of services, and include clinical audit, key worker activity, standard setting, user satisfaction surveys and local quality projects. The gender and ethnicity of service users is an important component of monitoring. However, there must be a strategic framework for all this activity or else good practice fails to be spread, effort is duplicated and initiatives may not be sustained.

149. Purchasers are increasingly involving users in service evaluation and this is an important way of ensuring that 'quality' is defined in ways which reflect users' concerns. It should be part of the structured approach to quality, rather than a series of ad hoc user satisfaction surveys and other initiatives. Users should be trained and supported to take part and information fed back to them. A clear policy regarding confidentiality and users' access to records should be established locally. The commissioner and provider should develop an integrated approach to quality, with the commissioner using the output from a structured quality management system put in place by the provider as evidence of quality.

Recommendation: Monitoring should be part of the purchasing strategy. Purchasers should request the reports from the national audits, as a first step, and establish a local framework for the collection of meaningful activity data which is also of use to clinicians and managers. Computer registers are becoming essential to the efficient management of such information.

Recommendations

1 Purchasers should make better use of all the potential sources of information on local needs, such as census data, FHSA lists and provider lists, and should adjust the pattern of resources accordingly.

2 Purchasers should develop clear strategic plans, which should include the balance of resources between hospital and different types of community service. They should set priorities, including defined need groups, such as those with long-term problems.

3 Local purchasing decisions should be based on consultation with the other major agencies in mental health in order to make the best use of resources. These include health providers, social services, housing, the criminal justice system, providers of employment and education services, as well as a range of interest groups, such as voluntary organisations and representatives of users and carers. Reviews of the balance of local provision should include the resources provided by all relevant agencies.

4 Joint commissioning between DHAs and FHSAs should be encouraged. All GPs, including fundholders, should be involved in the local mental health strategy and should be involved in care programmes for the individuals on their lists.

5 The procedures for care management and care programmes should be developed jointly between health and social services and should dovetail together.

6 The Government needs to work out the appropriate balance between health and social care and reconsider how to apportion funds between them.

7 Housing for people with mental health problems should be made available by local authority or housing associations, the living costs funded through the normal channels of social security benefits and the care provided, or at least funded, through health and social services. A national lead should be taken by the Departments of Health and the Environment together to provide more suitable housing for people with mental health problems. Local authority housing departments should also be working closely on this issue.

8 Planning for the care of mentally disordered offenders should involve all of the agencies working together and should consider the resource implications of diversion schemes and transfers from custody. Discussion between the Department of Health and the Home Office over funding is necessary at a national level.

9 Purchasers should have a clear plan of action for hospital closure, which should include a timetable of key dates, agreement on the financial arrangements and identification of the responsibilities for individuals who need to be resettled. Any resources released should be identified and retained for mental health.

10 Purchasers should work with providers to develop detailed and specific contracts which specify short, medium and long term targets.

11 Monitoring should be part of the purchasing strategy. Purchasers should request the reports from the national audits as a first step and establish a local framework for the collection of meaningful activity data.

Conclusion

150. The problems described in this report need a clear strategy set out in jointly agreed plans. These plans should:

- address the overall level of resources available;
- set out the mix and distribution of services required in hospital and the community;
- set out arrangements to improve the targeting of services;
- provide a framework for inter-agency cooperation – particularly where a hospital closure is planned; and
- translate these requirements into clear contracts with effective monitoring arrangements.

151. The main challenge is managerial rather than clinical. The managers of a developing service need to have good leadership skills and to take responsibility for both hospital and community services. The budgets should be transferable between the two. It will not be easy to achieve these goals. However, the prospect of improving the lot of some of the most disadvantaged members of society make it essential that the enterprise is a success.

Action Plan

1 **Central government should:**

- consider revising the resource allocation formula to DHAs to take special account of mental health, based on local needs;

- require professional training to be based more in the community with a focus on people with severe and long-term problems;

- bring the Department of Health, Home Office and Department of the Environment together to work out solutions to the problems of housing for people with mental health problems and mentally ill offenders; and

- consider how bridging finance could be made available for the reprovision of community care in place of some hospital care.

2 **District purchasers should:**

- establish effective local need assessment, incorporating census information and local case identification, via GPs and other providers;

- develop a mental health strategy in conjunction with providers, social services, the FHSA and primary care teams, criminal justice agencies and others;

- develop clear action plans for the closure of the targeted large hospitals, with a definite timetable, agreement over the funding arrangements and all of the resources retained for mental health; and

- develop detailed contracts with targets which can be monitored on a regular basis.

3 **Purchasers and providers should:**

- make use of local information on needs to distribute resources to different parts of the district;

- work out the appropriate mix of community and hospital services needed to meet the full range of individual needs;

- review the balance of expenditure on different types of service and explore the possibility of substituting alternatives to maximise cost effectiveness, especially within a full range of supported housing; and

- review the skill mix of the staff employed and investigate the scope for the employment of unqualified staff, with appropriate support.

4 **Provider managers should:**

- establish that those with severe mental illness are the service's priority and work with local teams to define the criteria for receiving a specialist service in hospital and in the community;

- appoint clinicians, especially psychiatrists, to work across both hospital and community to ensure continuity;

- give support to users and carers to enable them to participate in decisions;

- ensure that the CPA is fully established, working in conjunction with social services and others;

- establish proper management arrangements for community professionals and teams, incorporating caseload monitoring and review; and

- establish information systems which provide useful information on activities and needs to clinicians as well as for planning.

5 **FHSAs, GPs and primary care teams should:**

- be fully involved in the mental health strategy;

- participate in care programme arrangements for individuals, especially those with long-term needs; and

- take the main responsibility for those with less severe mental illnesses, with the FHSA providing guidance and support (and with support and training from the specialist services).

6 **Social services should:**

- be fully involved in the mental health strategy;

- participate in the care programme approach and link it with care management arrangements; and

- work with the health service on establishing the criteria for the CPA and care management.

7 **Housing agencies should:**

- give priority to people with mental health problems in the allocation of housing, in conjunction with the agencies involved in mental health care.

Glossary

The key professionals in mental health

Community mental health teams
provide assessment, treatment and care for individuals and groups, outside hospitals. They comprise a mix of the professionals described below but not all are represented in every team. CPNs are usually the most numerous.

Psychiatrists
are doctors who have specialised in mental health who work both in hospitals and, increasingly, in the community. They are responsible for diagnosis, the general mental health and physical care of patients, including medication, and have specific responsibilities in the implementation of the Mental Health Act. Some have further specialist training in areas such as the psychiatry of old age or psychotherapy.

Psychiatric nurses
are the most numerous professionals in mental health. Most of their basic training takes place in hospital.

Community psychiatric nurses (CPNs)
are usually Registered Mental Nurses, some of whom have completed the ENB training for community work. Their role can include psychological therapies, long-term support, counselling and administering medication by 'depot' injection.

Clinical psychologists
have a degree in psychology and a postgraduate qualification in clinical work. They have a key role in assessment and may carry out a wide range of treatments, such as behavioural therapy and cognitive therapy. They may provide training and supervision in this kind of work to other professionals.

Occupational therapists (OTs)
work in hospital and in the community. Their role is to help people to develop confidence and skills in daily living, using a variety of techniques such as creative therapies and training in practical tasks.

Social workers
have a general qualification in social work and may have specialised later in mental health. Approved social workers (**ASWs**) have undertaken specialist training in mental health and been approved by the local authority. They have statutory responsibilities when people are compulsorily admitted to hospital and have a duty to examine alternatives to hospitalisation.

74

Psychotherapists, psychoanalysts and counsellors
all offer 'talking treatments'. The methods, intensity of treatment and the
length of time involved varies. Individual or group therapy may be offered.
Many psychotherapists are also psychiatrists, psychologists or nurses.

GPs and primary care teams
are the main providers of care for people with less severe mental illness. They
also have an important role in the care of people with long-term and severe
mental illness.

Acute care
is treatment and care for people who are in an acute phase of their mental
illness or a psychiatric crisis. It does not necessarily entail hospital care.

Other Common Abbreviations

CHC	Community health council
CMHT	Community mental health team
CMHC	Community mental health centre
CPA	Care Programme Approach
DGH	District general hospital
DH	Department of Health
DHA	District health authority
FHSA	Family health services authority
GPFH	General practitioner fundholder
LA	Local authority
LASS	Local authority social services
MDT	Multi-disciplinary team
MHAC	Mental Health Act Commission
NHS	National Health Service
NHSE	NHS Executive (formerly NHSME)
OPCS	Office of Population Censuses and Surveys
PHCT	Primary health care team
RSU	Regional secure unit
SHA	Special health authority
SSD	Social services department
SSI	Social Services Inspectorate

Appendix 1 – Diagnostics

Diagnostic – health commissioners

Strategy and policy

Does the authority have a clear agenda for mental health with a strategy setting out how the mental health of the population is to be improved?

Does the authority have clear plans for community-based mental health services, which cover the full range of needs for people with mental health problems? (See trust diagnostic.) Do they reflect the need to reduce reliance on hospital beds as the main focus of the service?

Do the plans reflect the need:

◆ to link community and hospital services;

◆ to coordinate the different elements of care;

◆ to reflect the activity of primary care?

Does the strategy include clear, funded and timetabled plans for changes to service delivery?

Is the strategy shared with other important agencies: the FHSA, GPs and local authorities; and developed in collaboration with health care providers?

Needs assessment

Is the strategy based on a formal assessment of the mental health needs of the population?

Is there a shared view with the local authority of categories of mental health needs and their priorities, and are the authorities working together to this common agenda?

Is there any programme of review of the services currently being provided, to assess the extent to which they meet the needs of the population?

Commissioning plans and contracts

Do contracts set down:

◆ comprehensive information on the nature and level of services, which goes beyond traditional contract numbers;

◆ some means of monitoring contracts meaningfully;

◆ specifications for the quality of services?

Information and contract monitoring

Has the commissioner set down:

◆ indicators of structure, process and, where possible, outcomes which will indicate progress toward strategic objectives;

◆ indicators that are agreed in collaboration with providers, relying on a variety of data sources including the views of service users?

Liaison with others

Is the commissioner aware of its relative position in terms of provision and staffing of mental health services? Can it explain the position?

Has the commissioner developed its strategic approach in collaboration with other agencies, the voluntary sector and in consultation with service users?

Are arrangements in place at an operational level to ensure that services are delivered as seamlessly as possible, for example, in the provision and financing of services for people with severe and long-term mental health problems? Is there a mechanism for monitoring this?

Diagnostic – NHS trusts

Strategic direction, needs assessment and information for contract monitoring are shared areas of responsibility with health authority commissioners. These should be developed in a collaborative framework, since trusts are often in the best position to gather local information on needs, service delivery and outcomes, to support the broader information used by purchasers.

Strategy and policy

Does the trust have a clear agenda for mental health with a strategy setting out how the mental health of the population is to be improved?

Does the trust have clear plans for community-based mental health services, which cover the full range of needs of people with mental health problems?

Do the plans reflect the need:

◆ to link community and hospital services;

◆ to coordinate the different elements of care;

◆ to reflect the activity of the primary care sector?

Does the strategy include clear, funded and timetabled plans for changes to service delivery?

Is the strategy developed in collaboration with health commissioners and shared with other important agencies: the FHSA, GPs and local authorities?

Needs assessment

Is the strategy based on some assessment of the mental health needs of the population?

Is there a shared view agreed with the commissioner and the local authority of categories of mental health needs and their priorities and are the agencies working together on this common agenda?

Is there any programme of review of the services currently provided to assess the extent to which they meet the needs of the population?

Information and monitoring

Does the trust supply:

- indicators of structure, process and, where possible, outcomes which will indicate progress toward strategic objectives;
- indicators that are agreed in collaboration with commissioners, relying on a variety of data sources including the views of service users?

Service delivery

Is there a full range of services in the community to meet the needs of people with mental health problems?

- assessment of needs;
- community mental health teams supporting mentally ill people in their own homes as far as possible, including the provision of emergency out-of-hours services and crisis response;
- links with primary care services;
- information for service users and their carers;
- support to carers;
- employment, retraining and placement services;
- day services;
- residential and non-residential respite services;
- places in health, local authority and independent sector hostels, residential care homes, sheltered housing, supported lodgings or other similar provision for people needing residential care outside hospital;
- in-patient services for those who require short-term hospital admission, and for the longer-term treatment, including asylum, of those few for whom there is no suitable alternative?

These services may be provided by different service providers but the trust should have access to the full range so that care can be planned and coordinated for individuals.

- Are hospital and community services managed as part of the same service so that admission to hospital is considered as the last resort rather than the point of entry to the service?
- Are there clear policies for each element of the service so that professionals know their target client group?
- Have people with severe and long-term mental health problems been identified so that services can be planned around their needs?
- Are there mechanisms for monitoring these policies in practice and for managing the caseloads of teams and workers?
- Has the care programme approach been effectively implemented to ensure that services are planned and coordinated for those people with the most complex needs?

- Are there clear inter-agency procedures for planning and delivering care programmes? Do these include an initial screen for all service users, followed by a multi-disciplinary assessment for people with complex needs?
- Are streamlined processes in place for agreeing funding and provision responsibilities for people with severe and long-term mental health problems?
- Are users involved in planning and evaluating services, both at an overall level and for their own individual care?

Diagnostic – FHSAs

Does the authority have a clear, written strategic direction for adult mental health services? Was it developed in collaboration with and agreed by health commissioners, social services departments and GPs?

Has the FHSA been involved in any joint review of the services currently provided? Have services been adjusted to reflect this?

Is there a policy on the interface between primary and secondary care?

Are practices encouraged to develop practice policies or protocols on mental health and to agree these with the secondary service?

Is there a policy on the provision of counselling in primary care?

Diagnostic – GP fundholders

Strategy and policy

Does the practice have a clear agenda for mental health with a strategy setting out how the mental health of the practice population is to be improved?

Is the strategy shared with other important agencies, the health authority and the FHSA, and developed in collaboration with health care providers?

Does the strategy take account of the views of service users and their carers?

Needs assessment

Does the practice have information about the mental health needs of its population and especially about the small number of people with serious mental health problems?

Is this information readily available to all practice staff?

Contracts

Do contracts set down:

- comprehensive information on the nature and level of services to be provided, which goes beyond traditional contract numbers;
- some means of monitoring contracts meaningfully;
- specifications for the quality of services?

Are arrangements in place at an operational level to ensure that services are delivered as seamlessly as possible, for example, by establishing formal links between the practice and its local community mental health team?

Diagnostic – Social Services

Strategic direction

Does the authority have a clear, written strategic direction for adult mental health services:

- developed in collaboration with and agreed by health commissioners and trusts, the public and the voluntary sector; and
- reflecting the policy of community care, with a range of flexible, community-based services to meet the needs of people with mental health problems? (See trust diagnostic.)

Is this backed up by clear, timetabled objectives for service development, again in collaboration with other relevant agencies and reflecting the need to reduce reliance on hospital beds as the main focus of the service?

Needs-based approach

Does the authority have a needs-led rather than a service-driven culture with individual workers having the capacity to package services in relation to need?

Has the authority assessed the needs of people with mental health problems in the area, in collaboration with other agencies and interested parties?

Has the authority established local categories of need to help in planning and delivering services, in accordance with the strategic direction? Are these shared with the health commissioner?

Has the authority ensured that people with the most severe mental health problems have been identified?

Appropriate information at senior management level

Do senior managers routinely receive information on key activities of the department which enables them to assess important quality issues?

For example:

- delays before assessment;
- numbers of people receiving care by category of need;
- variations in practice between teams?

Management arrangements to support the strategic direction

Do the management arrangements reflect the philosophy of the NHS and Community Care Act and promote best practice:

- with specialist workers for mental health problems;
- with a mechanism to monitor workloads for field workers;
- with built-in flexibility that allows workers to put together packages of services, according to the needs of individuals with mental health problems and their carers?

Joint working

Has the authority reviewed the existing pattern of services jointly with the relevant health agencies?

Has the inter-agency review been published, setting out the agenda for future service developments in relation to needs?

Has the authority agreed with the relevant health agencies who will be responsible for what services?

Have patterns of service been altered in the light of these decisions?

Do mental health social workers work in multi-disciplinary community mental health teams with their colleagues from the NHS?

Are the assessment procedures for care management and the care programme approach integrated?

Policy in practice

Is the authority aware of its relative position in terms of expenditure per head of population on services for people with mental health problems? Can it explain the variation?

Appendix 2 – Calculation of Savings

In-patient beds

Total number of mental illness beds in England	47,296
Adult	26,195
Secure	1,025
Elderly	19,447
Children	629
Total cost of adult beds	£1,136 m pa
Cost per bed	£43,370 pa

The cost of beds is probably overstated because medical staff and other staff who work across the whole adult mental health service (in hospital and in the community) are included as a cost of the in-patient service only. There are also doubts about the apportionment of capital and overheads which are included in expenditure figures.

The average cost of an acute bed for our study sites was calculated as £32,000 and this figure has been used as a conservative estimate for this calculation.

12% reduction in number of beds	3,140
Average cost per bed	£32,000 pa
Total funds released	£100 m

Average costs were used in this exercise rather than marginal costs. This is felt to be legitimate because of the numbers of beds involved; more than 3,000 beds across England translates to an average of one ward per district and in practice the 'excess' beds will tend to be clustered more than this. Changes on this scale mean wholesale shifts in the pattern of services.

All figures are for 1992-93.

Residential accommodation

A sample of 43 districts in England found a median level of 11.1 NHS and jointly provided residential places per 100,000 population[1].

This suggests a total of 5,200 places nationally.

According to the same survey, 77% of residential places had 24-hour staffing.

[1]
A Survey of Adult Mental Health Services, Faulkner A, Field V, Muijen M, Sainsbury Centre for Mental Health 1994

One of our study sites provides a range of supported residential places, including 14% with 24-hour staffing. The costs of these places are as follows:

Average cost per place for all levels of support	£7,100 pa
Average cost per place for 24-hour staffing	£18,300 pa
Average cost per place for range of less intensive support	£5,300 pa

If the pattern of care nationally could change from a high proportion of places with 24-hour staffing to the pattern offered by this site, the resources which could be released are as follows:

Cost of 77% of places with 24-hour support:

(5,200 x 0.77) x £18,300	£73.3 m

Cost of 14% of places with 24-hour support + 63% of places with a range of support:

(5,200 x 0.14) x £18,300	£13.3 m
(5,200 x 0.63) x £5,300	£17.3 m
Total cost of new pattern	£30.6 m

Funds released	£42.5m

This would fund an additional 6,000 places at the overall average cost per place, including 840 with 24-hour staffing.

All costs are for 1992-93.

Health care assistants

CPN numbers and grades

In 1992 there were 4,250 CPNs in England[I] and an estimated 275 in Wales[II].

In 1990 research found that 75% of CPNs were at grade G, with 11% above this and 15% below[III.] We have therefore assumed a total cost equivalent to 4,500 CPNs at G grade.

Cost per client hour

Each G grade nurse costs £21,000 pa, inclusive of NI and superannuation.

Assuming that each CPN works 46 weeks per year and spends 20 hours per week in contact with clients, then the cost per client hour is £22.83.

Nationally CPNs deliver 4.14 million hours of care each year at a total cost of £94.5 million.

Scope for substitution by health care assistants

Assuming that health care assistants could deliver 20% of this care, this would mean 0.828 million hours of care per annum.

Assuming that health care assistants (HCAs) work 46 weeks per year and spend 30 hours per week in contact with clients, then this amount of care would require 600 HCAs to be appointed. Experience in other skill mix exercises has shown that staff on lower grades tend to spend more time in direct contact with clients.

Each HCA at A grade costs £9,320 pa, inclusive of NI and superannuation. The total cost of this care would be £5.6 million pa.

This would release £13.3 million pa, which would fund an additional 1,400 HCA posts or 630 CPN posts.

I

Health Committee, *First Report, Session 1993-94, Better off in the Community? The care of people who are seriously mentally ill,* HMSO 1994

II

Calculated from 1990 figures, assuming same rate of growth as for England.

III

3rd Quinquennial National Community Psychiatric Nursing survey, Edward White, University of Manchester 1990

Appendix 3 – The Advisory Group

Thanks are due for the advice and guidance of the following people, who were members of the external advisory group to the project:

Judith Baptiste – National Schizophrenia Fellowship

Virginia Beardshaw – Director of Commissioning, Barnet Health Authority

Marion Beeforth – User of mental health services

Jennifer Bernard – Director of Social Services, Newcastle City Council

Tony Butterworth – Professor of Nursing, Manchester University

Edna Conlan – User of mental health services and representative of UKAN

Dewi Evans – Director of Social Services, Dyfed County Council

Cliff Graham – Centre for Mental Health Services Development

Rachel Jenkins – Principal Medical Officer, Department of Health

Lionel Joyce – Chief Executive, Newcastle City Health NHS Trust

Tony Kendrick – Research Fellow, Department of General Practice, St. George's Hospital Medical School

Frank Kerkam – District auditor

David King – Leader of the Mental Health Task Force

David Kingdon – Senior Medical Officer, Department of Health

Andrew McCullough – Assistant Secretary, Department of Health

Parimala Moodley – Consultant psychiatrist

Elaine Murphy – Mental Health Act Commission member, Professor and Consultant psychiatrist, York Clinic

Liz Sayce – Director of Policy and Information, MIND

Geoff Shepherd – Head of Research, Sainsbury Centre for Mental Health

Geraldine Strathdee – Consultant psychiatrist, Maudsley Hospital

Chris Thompson – Registrar of the Royal College of Psychiatry, Professor of Psychiatry, Southampton

References

1. D.Goldberg and P.Huxley, *Common Mental Disorders*, Routledge, 1992.

2. F.Oyebode, S.Cumella, G.Garden, S.Binyon, Diagnosis-related Groups: Implications for Psychiatry, *Psychiatric Bulletin*, 14, 1-3, 1990.

3. DHSS, *Better Services for the Mentally Ill*, HMSO, 1975.

4. DH, *Caring for People*, HMSO, 1989.

5. DH, The Care Programme Approach, HC(90)23, HMSO, 1990.

6. DH, *Health of the Nation, Key Area Handbook, Mental Health*, HMSO, 1993.

7. Welsh Office, *Mental Illness: Strategy for Wales*, HMSO,1989.

8. Welsh Office, *Protocol for Investment in Health Gain: Mental Health*, 1993.

9. J.Ritchie, D.Dick, R.Lingham, *The Report of the Inquiry into the Care and Treatment of Christopher Clunis*, HMSO, 1994.

10. Steering Committee of the Confidential Enquiry into Homicides and Suicides by Mentally Ill People, *A Preliminary Report on Homicide*, 1994.

11. P.White, Home Office statistician, personal communication, 1994.

12. Mental Health Foundation, *Creating Community Care*, Mental Health Foundation, 1994.

13. G.Glover, E.Robin, J.Emami and R.Arabsheibani, *The Distribution of Need for Mental Health Services - A Study of the Socio-Demographic Predictors of Prevalence of Psychiatric Admission in a London Region*, Final Report to the Department of Health of a Project commissioned under the Research and Development Initiative, 1994.

14. B.Jarman, S.Hirsch, Statistical Models to Predict District Psychiatric Morbidity, in G.Thornicroft, C.Brewin and J.Wing (eds), *Measuring Mental Health Needs*, Gaskell, 1992.

15. B. Jarman, S.Hirsch, P.White, R.Driscoll, Predicting Psychiatric Admission Rates, *British Medical Journal*, 304, 1146-1151, 1992.

16. R.Powell, D.Hollander, R.Tobiansky, A Longitudinal Survey of the Bedstate of the Acute Psychiatric Units in North London: 1990-1993, paper presented at the Winter meeting of the Royal College of Psychiatrists, 1994.

17. P.Lelliot, Monitoring Inner London Mental Health Services, Royal College of Psychiatrists, unpublished, 1994.

18. G.Thornicroft, O.Margolius, D.Jones, The TAPS Project,. 6: New Long-stay Psychiatric Patients and Social Deprivation, *British Journal of Psychiatry*, 161, 621-624, 1992.

19. R.Kammerling and S.O'Connor, Unemployment Rate as a Predictor of Rate of Psychiatric Admission, *British Medical Journal*, 307, 1536-1539, 1993.

20 Mental Health Task Force, *Mental Health in London: Priorities for Action*, Mental Health Task Force, 1994

21. P.Campbell, J.Taylor, C.Pantelis, C.Harvey, Studies of Schizophrenia in a Large Mental Hospital Proposed for Closure and in Two Halves of an Inner London Borough Served by the Hospital, in M.Weller (ed), *International Perspectives in Schizophrenia*, John Libbey, 1990.

22. C.Pantelis, P.Campbell, The South Camden Schizophrenia Survey, *Bulletin of the Royal College of Psychiatrists*, 12, 98-101, 1988.

23. S.Turner and C.Haskins, London Capitation Weighting: Social Deprivation, Homelessness and Mental Health, *Psychiatric Bulletin*, 17, 641-646, 1993.

24. D.McGovern and R.Cope, First Psychiatric Admission Rates of First and Second Generation Afro-Caribbeans, *Social Psychiatry*, 22, 139-149, 1987

25. D.McGovern and R.Cope, Second Generation Afro-Caribbeans and Young Whites with a First Admission of Schizophrenia, *Social Psychiatry and Psychiatric Epidemiology*, 26, 95-99, 1991.

26. M.Wilson, *Mental Health and Britain's Black Communities*, NHSME, Prince of Wales Advisory Group on Disability and Kings Fund Centre, 1993.

27. C.Thomas, K.Stone, M.Osborn, P.Thomas and M.Fisher, Psychiatric Morbidity and Compulsory Admission Among UK-Born Europeans, Afro-Caribbeans and Asians in Central Manchester, *British Journal of Psychiatry*, 163, 91-99, 1993.

28. A. Davis, A Constructive Escape Route: Who Wants Day Care?, in *Day Care Information Pack*, Good Practices in Mental Health, 1989.

29. J.Carson and T.Sharma, In-patient Psychiatric Care What Helps? Staff and Patient Perspectives, *Journal of Mental Health*, 3, 99-104, 1994.

30. B.Lazarides, I.Bibou, A.Benos, A.Iacovides, C.Ierodiakonou, Community Mental Health Services Needs Assessment of Families with Psychotic Members, paper presented at 4th International Conference on Innovations in Community Psychiatry, York, 1994.

31. M.Beiser, J.Shore, R.Peters, E.Tatum, Does Community Care for the Mentally Ill Make a Difference? A Tale of Two Cities, *American Journal of Psychiatry*, 142:9, 1047-1052, 1985.

32. F.Baker, D.Jodrey, J.Intagliata, H.Straus, Community Support Services and Functioning of the Seriously Mentally Ill, *Community Mental Health Journal*, 29:4, 321-331, 1993.

33. S.Kavanagh, Estimating the prevalence of Schizophrenia: a Model for Service Development and Evaluation, submitted for publication to *Journal of Public Health Medicine*, 1994.

34. J.Turner Crowson, *Reshaping Mental Health Services. Implications for Britain of US Experiences*, Kings Fund Institute, 1993.

35. L.Stein and M.Test, Alternative to Mental Hospital Treatment I, *Archives of General Psychiatry*, 37, 392-397, 1980.

36. B.Weisbrod, M.Test and L.Stein, Alternative to Mental Hospital Treatment II: Economic Benefit-cost analysis, *Archives of General Psychiatry*, 37, 400-405, 1980.

37. J.Hoult, Community Care of the Acutely Mentally Ill, *British Journal of Psychiatry*, 149, 137-144, 1986.

38. C.Dean, J.Phillips, E.Gadd, M.Joseph and S.England, Comparison of Community-based Service with Hospital Based Service for People with Acute, Severe Psychiatric Illness, *British Medical Journal*, 307, 473-476, 1993.

39. M.Muijen, I.Marks, J.Connelly, B.Audini, Home-based Care and Standard Hospital Care for Patients with Severe Mental Illness: a Randomised Controlled Trial, *British Medical Journal*, 304, 749-54, 1992.

40. S. Merson, P.Tyrer, S.Onyett, S.Lack, P.Birkett, S.Lynch and T.Johnson, Early Intervention in Psychiatric emergencies: a Controlled Clinical Trial, *Lancet*, 339, 1311-1314, 1992.

41. T.Burns, A.Beadsmore, A.Bhat, A.Oliver, and C.Mathers, A Controlled Trial of Home-Based Acute Psychiatric Services, I & II, *British Journal of Psychiatry*, 163, 49-61, 1993.

42. L.Bachrach, Overview: Model Programs for Chronic Mental Patients, *American Journal of Psychiatry*, 137:9, 1023-1031, 1980.

43. L.Sayce, T.Craig, A.Boardman, The Development of Community Mental Health Centres in the UK, *Social Psychiatry and Psychiatric Epidemiology*, 26, 14-20, 1991.

44. G.Jackson, R.Gater, D.Goldberg, D.Tantum, L.Loftus and H.Taylor, A New Community Mental Health Team Based in Primary Care: a Description of the Service and its Effect on Service Use in the First Year, *British Journal of Psychiatry*, 162, 375-384, 1993.

45. C.Vassilas and H.Gethin Morgan, General Practitioner's Contact with Victims of Suicide, *British Medical Journal*, 307, 300-301, 1993.

46. T.Kendrick, T.Burns, P.Freeling and B.Sibbald, The Provision of Care to Patients with Disabling Long-term Mental Illnesses; a Survey in 16 Practices, *British Journal of General Practice*, 44, 301-305, 1994.

47. R.Jenkins, Developments in the Primary Care of Mental Illness: a Forward Look, *International Review of Psychiatry*, 4, 237-242, 1992.

48. L.Gask, Training General Practitioners to Detect and Manage Emotional Disorders, *International Review of Psychiatry*, 4, 293-300, 1992.

49. W.Rutz, L.von Knorring and J. Wallinder, Long-term Effects of an Educational Program for General Practitioners Given by the Swedish Committee for the Prevention and Treatment of Depression, *Acta Psychiatrica Scandinavica*, 85, 83-88, 1992.

50. D.Gath and J.Catalan, The Treatment of Emotional Disorders in General Practice; Psychological Methods Versus Medication, *Journal of Psychosomatic Research*, 30, 381-386, 1986.

51. R.Thomas and R.Corney, The Role of the Practice Nurse in Mental Health: a Survey, *Journal of Mental Health*, 2, 65-72, 1993.

52. I.Marks, Controlled Trial of Psychiatric Nurse Therapists in Primary Care, *British Medical Journal*, 290, 1181, 1985.

53. N.Freemantle, F.Song, T.Sheldon, P.Watson, J.Mason and A. Long, Managing Depression in Primary Care, *Quality in Health Care*, 2, 58-62, 1993.

54. MIND, *MIND's Policy on Primary Care, Policy Pack*, MIND, 1993.

55. R.Corney, The Effectiveness of Attached Social Workers in the Management of Depressed Female Patients in General Practice, *Psychological Medicine*, 14 (Monograph supplement 6), 47, 1984.

56. J.Holden, R.Sagovsky and J.Cox, Counselling in a General Practice Setting: Controlled Study of Health Visitor Intervention in Treatment of Post-natal Depression, *British Medical Journal*, 298, 223-226, 1989.

57. B.Sibbald, J.Addington-Hall, D.Brenneman and P.Freeling, Counsellors in English and Welsh General Practices: their Nature and Distribution, *British Medical Journal*, 306, 29-33, 1993.

58. K.Gournay and J.Brooking, A Prospective Randomised Controlled Trial of the Efficacy of CPNs and GPs in Treating Patients with Minor Psychiatric Disorder in Primary Care, Report to the Department of Health, 1991.

59. T.Kendrick, B.Sibbald, T.Burns and P.Freeling, Role of General Practitioners in the Care of Long-term Mentally Ill Patients, *British Medical Journal*, 302, 508-510, 1991.

60. E.Johnstone, D.Owens, A.Gold, T.Crow, J.Macmillan, Schizophrenic Patients Discharged from Hospital: A Follow-up Study, *British Journal of Psychiatry* 145, 586-590, 1984.

61. A.Mitchell, Psychiatrists in Primary Health Care Settings, *British Journal of Psychiatry*, 147, 371-379, 1985.

62. P.Tyrer, N.Sievewright and S.Wollerton, General Practice Psychiatric Clinics: Impact on Psychiatric Services, *British Journal of Psychiatry*, 145, 15-19, 1984.

63. G.Strathdee, Psychiatrists in Primary Care: the General Practitioner Viewpoint, *Family Practice*, 5, 111-115, 1988.

64. G.Strathdee, personal communication.

65. T.Kendrick, B.Sibbald, J.Addington-Hall, D.Brenneman and P.Freeling, Distribution of Mental Health Professionals Working on Site in English and Welsh General Practices, *British Medical Journal*, 307, 544-546, 1993.

66. D.Goldberg, A.Mann, D.Pilgrim, A.Rogers, D.Sharp, K.Sutherby, G.Strathdee, G.Thornicroft and T.Wykes, Developing a Strategy for a

Primary Care focus for Mental Health Services, Report to SELHA, November 1993.

67. C.Patmore and T.Weaver, *Community Mental Health Teams:Lessons for Planners and Managers*, Good Practices in Mental Health, 1991.

68. K.Wooff, D.Goldberg and T. Fryers, Patients in Receipt of Community Psychiatric Nursing Care in Salford 1976-82, *Psychological Medicine*, 16, 407-414, 1986.

69. E.White, Surveying CPNs, *Nursing Times*, 86: 51, 62-64, 1990.

70. P.Bebbington and S.Feeney, The Use of In-patient beds in the Joint Hospital: Report of an Audit of Bed Usage, Report to the Maudsley Hospital, 1992.

71. D. Tantam, R,Gater, G.Jackson, S.Amaee, H.Fitzgerald, C.Perceval, R.Purlackee and M.Stratton, Auditing the Community Team, *Journal of Mental Health*, 1:4, 327-334, 1992.

72. N.Fulop, J.Koffman and M.Hudson, Challenging Bed Behaviours: the Use of Acute Psychiatric Beds in an Inner London District Health Authority, *Journal of Mental Health*, 1:4, 1992.

73. H.Miller and M.Turner, Home Truths, *Health Service Journal,* 9th September, 1993.

74. C.O'Driscoll, J.Marshall and J.Reed, Chronically Ill Psychiatric Patients in a District General Hospital Unit: a Survey and Two-Year Follow-up in an Inner-London Health District, *British Journal of Psychiatry*, 157, 694-702, 1990.

75. DH, Guidelines on Supervised Discharge, HSG(94)27, 1994.

76. M.Beeforth, E.Conlan, R.Graley and V.Field, *Have We Got Views for You, User Evaluation of Case Management*, Sainsbury Centre for Mental Health, 1994.

77. Department of Health, *Working in Partnership, Report of the Mental Health Nursing Review Team,* HMSO, 1994.

78. N.Tarrier, C.Barrowclough, C.Vaughn, J.Bamrah, K.Porceddu, S.Watts and H.Freeman, Community Management of Schizophrenia: a Two-Year Follow-up of a Behavioural Intervention with Families, *British Journal of Psychiatry*, 154, 625-628, 1989.

79. C.Brooker, Meeting the Needs of Families, *Nursing*, 4: 29, 13-16, 1991.

80. I.Falloon, *Family Management of Schizophrenia: a controlled Study of Clinical, Social, Family and Economic Benefits*, John Hopkins University Press, Baltimore, 1985.

81. M.Birchwood, Early Intervention in Schizophrenia: Theoretical Background and Clinical Strategies, *British Journal of Clinical Psychology*, 31, 257-278, 1992.

82. T.Butterworth, Developing Research Ideas from Theory into Practice, Psychosocial Intervention as a Case Example, *Nurse Researcher*, 1: 4, 78-86, 1994.

83. G.Shepherd, Case Management, *Health Trends*, 22: 2, 59-61, 1990.

84. R. Ford, personal communication.

85. A.Walid and M.McCarthy, Community Psychiatric Care for Homeless People in Inner London, *Health Trends*, 37, 392-397, 1989.

86. P.Timms and A.Fry, Homelessness and Mental Illness, *Health Trends*, 21, 70-71, 1989.

87. House of Commons Health Committee, *Better Off in the Community? The Care of People who are Seriously Mentally Ill, Minutes of Evidence and Appendices*, HMSO, 1994.

88. F.Keating, O.Klein, P.Manning and M.Ratcliffe, *The Homelessness and Mental Health Initiative: One Year On*, Research and Development for Psychiatry, 1992.

89. P.Carling, Housing and Supports for Persons with Mental Illness: Emerging Approaches to Research and Practice, *Hospital and Community Psychiatry*, 44: 5, 1993.

90. Home Office, *Provision for Mentally Disordered Offenders*, Circular 66/90, 1990.

91. DH and Home Office, *Review of Health and Social services for Mentally Disordered Offenders and Others Requiring Similar Services*, Cmnd 2088, HMSO, 1992.

92. S.Blumenthal and S.Wessely, National Survey of Current Arrangements for Diversion from Custody in England and Wales, *British Medical Journal*, 305, 1322-1325, 1992.

93. D.James and L.Hamilton, The Clerkenwell Scheme: Assessing Efficacy and Cost of a Psychiatric Liaison Scheme to a Magistrate's Court, *British Medical Journal*, 303, 282-285, 1991.

94. M.Knapp, J.Beecham, A.Hallam, A.Fenyo, The Costs of Community Care for Former Long-stay Psychiatric Hospital Residents, *Health and Social Care*, 1, 193-201, 1993.

95. Association of Metropolitan Authorities, *Mental Health Services: Issues for Local Government*, AMA, 1993.

96. M.Knapp, J.Beecham, J.Anderson, D.Dayson, J.Leff, O.Margolius, C.O'Driscoll and W.Wills, The TAPS Project, 3: Predicting the Community Costs of Closing Psychiatric Hospitals, *British Journal of Psychiatry*, 157, 661-670, 1990.

97. TAPS Research Unit, *The Eighth Annual Conference of the Team for the Assessment of Psychiatric Services: Summary of Proceedings*, July, 1993.

Index *References are to paragraph numbers*